SOLAR

£2.49

32/-

mm

35

By the same author

The Law for Everyman
(Collins 1963)

Man and his Kind
(Darton, Longman & Todd 1973, Praeger, 1973)

The Phenomenon of Money
(Routledge & Kegan Paul, 1980)

The Death of an Emperor
(Constable 1989, OUP Paperback 1990)

The Anthropology of Numbers
(Cambridge University Press, 1991)

The Japanese Numbers Game
(Routledge, 1992)

SOLAR ECLIPSE

Thomas Crump

Constable · London

First published in Great Britain 1999
by Constable and Company Limited
3 The Lanchesters, 162 Fulham Palace Road
London W6 9ER
Copyright © Thomas Crump 1999
ISBN 0 09 479170 8
The right of Thomas Crump to be identified as author
of this work has been asserted by him in accordance
with the Copyright, Designs and Patents Act 1988

Set in Monotype Imprint 11pt by
Rowland Phototypesetting Ltd
Printed in Great Britain by
St Edmundsbury Press Ltd
both of Bury St Edmunds, Suffolk

A CIP catalogue record for this book
is available from the British Library

Contents

Acknowledgements

The author and publisher are grateful to Cambridge University Press for permission to reproduce illustrative material from F.R. Stephenson, *Historical Eclipses and Earth's Rotation* (1997): figures 1.3 and 6.2, and gratefully acknowledge HM Nautical Almanac Office as the source of figure 2.1. and the Goddard Space Flight Centre of the US National Aeronautical and Space Administration as the source of figure 6.4.

Preface

Letter from the author to his daughter

Dear Laurien,

Early one morning in the summer of 1986, when we were on our way to a holiday in Switzerland, we had just come out of a tunnel – about an hour after crossing the frontier – to see in the distance the mountains of the Oberland, glinting in the sunlight. Your brother Maarten, then twelve years old, hardly found time to look up from the popular science magazine he was reading. Instead, he asked us, 'What will be significant about 11 August 1999?' I found the answer immediately: 'That will be Laurien's twenty-first birthday.'

Maarten was nonplussed for a moment, although he had to admit that I was right. He then added, 'On that day there will be the first total eclipse of the Sun visible from Holland since the year 1440.' I must say that I was impressed, and since then I have been going over in my mind what to do about this remarkable *conjunction*, to use a favourite word of astronomers. This book is the result.

In the course of researching it I found that Maarten (or rather the magazine he was reading) was mistaken on two important points: there was no total eclipse of the Sun visible from Holland (then part of the Dukedom of Burgundy) in 1440, and the 1999 eclipse will not be total anywhere in Holland (although the whole country will get quite dark sometime around midday). The first mistake does not matter, and the second can be corrected since the south-west of England will lie under the path of totality on your twenty-first birthday. What we shall then see (from the house we have booked in Devon) is described in Chapter 1 of my book – provided that the weather (always chancy with solar eclipses) is not too unfavourable.

Since you enjoyed my last book, *The Anthropology of Numbers*, as much as anyone else I know, I think you will enjoy *Solar Eclipse*. Needless to say, it will not be the only eclipse book on sale in 1999; I already have quite a collection. They are all remarkably similar, with pages of numerical tables, chronologies of past and future eclipses, and maps of the path traced across the Earth by the Moon's shadow as it races by.

These books are for the amateur astronomer, but mine is written for those, like yourself, who are more interested in people than stars and other heavenly bodies. Sometimes the mathematics makes the going rather heavy (particularly in Chapters 2 and 6), but it is nothing compared to the endless columns of handwritten figures I have looked at in the archives (dating back to the seventeenth century) of the former Royal Greenwich Observatory. (Somewhat paradoxically it ended up in Cambridge, where the British government closed it down this last October – as if to make sure that it was not in business for the eclipse of 1999. *The RGO Guide to the 1999 Total Eclipse of the Sun* may be taken as sort of legacy.)

John Flamsteed, the first Astronomer Royal, was interested in eclipses, as is apparent from a letter written to him by the physicist Stephen Gray in 1699, containing a sketch of the path of the eclipse expected on 3 May 1715 – the last time, incidentally, that the path of totality crossed London. Flamsteed's successors continued to be interested in eclipses, sometimes passionately, particularly after the invention of photography, some 160 years ago, made it possible to record the sky as it appears during the few minutes for which the Sun is totally hidden by the Moon. To judge from his letters, Sir Frank Dyson, Astronomer Royal in the early years of the twentieth century, was interested in little else. This is not altogether surprising, since he was intent on British astronomers winning the race to prove the correctness of Einstein's General Theory of Relativity by photographing the stars appearing close to the Sun at the time of a total eclipse. And if you find the occasional maths in my book difficult, it is as nothing to the tensor calculus required by Einstein's theory. Take heart from the words of Einstein: 'Do not worry about your difficulties in mathematics; I can assure you that mine are still greater.'

One important point to be made is that astronomy has always worked with its own version of geometry. In observational astronomy angles matter as much as distances, so that, for instance, the angle that the apparent paths of the Sun and Moon make with the horizon at the time of an eclipse is just as significant as the distance of either from the Earth. Added confusion comes from the fact that a degree of arc, like an hour of time, is divided into 60 minutes, with every minute divided into 60 seconds. One rotation of the Earth defines a complete circle of 360 degrees of arc and a day of 24 hours – so that astronomers sometimes use a coordinate system in which 1 hour is the equivalent of 15 (360 divided by 24) degrees. In this book, when I mean time I write hours, minutes and seconds, and when I mean an angle I use the shorthand notation °, ' and ", so that, for example, the Earth, in a period of 2 hours, 3 minutes and 11 seconds, rotates through an angle of 30° 47' 45".

One result of a geometry based upon angles is that the sky is reduced to two dimensions – which has always been how people have perceived it. (If it were otherwise, there would be no constellations as we know them.) This means that a celestial globe, generally showing white stars on a black or dark blue background, shows stars on the surface of a virtual sphere whose centre is the Sun; an observer within the Solar System looks at this sphere from the inside. As a result, two heavenly bodies can often appear to be in the same place: this phenomenon, generally known as *conjunction*, is bound to happen when three dimensions are reduced to two. The two bodies are of course nowhere near each other, since their actual distances from the observer are quite different.

Such a conjunction between the Sun and the Moon produces an eclipse. To avoid confusion, it is often better to look at the system comprising the Sun, the Earth and the Moon from the outside, and from a perspective based on three dimensions. To do this to greatest advantage, it is best not to use an atlas of the heavens, or a celestial globe, but an *orrery*, a three-dimensional working model of the Sun, the planets and their moons. I bought mine as a kit for about £20 at the shop at Flamsteed House, the site of the original Greenwich Observatory. Putting the kit together was one of the more challenging tasks that accompanied the writing of this book.

Surprisingly for a subject like astronomy, which demands a very high level of accuracy, I have discovered any number of mistakes in the works I have consulted, and I fear that in my own book a number of mistakes have got in despite my careful double-checking. As any author must, I ask my readers to forgive me. On one point I disagree strongly with a widely accepted proposition, which is that one of the purposes of Stonehenge was to predict eclipses. Fred Hoyle, whom I knew as a young lecturer when I was reading maths at Cambridge nearly fifty years ago, wrote a whole book to show how Stonehenge could be used for this purpose. He is not alone. None the less, I am sure that he, and the many who accept his view, are mistaken, and I explain why in Chapter 3. Given the great number of people (including all the proponents of the big bang theory of the origin of the Universe) who have disagreed with Fred Hoyle in the first eighty odd years of his life, he will hardly be worried by my views on Stonehenge (which are also those of specialists like the historian of astronomy John North). My own conviction that Stonehenge, and other similar prehistoric monuments (of which there are many in the British Isles and north-west Europe) is borne out of my research for *The Anthropology of Numbers*. This book contains a fair dose of anthropology, which is to be found nowhere else – and which you, and many others, should enjoy.

You might also like to know that Eclipse, one of the greatest racehorses in history, got his name from the fact that he was foaled on the day, 1 April 1764, of a solar eclipse. His owner was the Prince of Wales, who later became King George IV. In his day he was even more famous than his infamous owner: the Eclipse Stakes, which are still run every year, were named after him, and in the United States the Eclipse Awards go to the top horses of the year.

As you will discover when you get down to writing your own books, the task is impossible without the help of any number of people (and in this last decade of the second millennium, the services of e-mail and the World Wide Web). I have been helped by astronomers, notably Adam Perkins, curator of the archives of the Royal Greenwich Observatory; Frédéric Clette and his colleagues at the Royal Observatory in Brussels, the leading European centre for research in solar physics; anthropologists, notably Gary Gossen (who referred me to a picture of a solar eclipse drawn by one of his, and also my, informants in Mexico) and

Andrew Strathern (who put me wise on New Guinea, where solar eclipses could be observed in two successive years in the mid-1980s); and many friends, including Christopher Courtauld, Yvonne Loster and Leon Mestel (himself a noted astronomer, renowned for his work on stars billions of times farther away from the Sun), who made helpful suggestions. At the very last moment I was able to visit Fred Espenak at the Goddard Space Flight Center just outside Washington. Like anyone working with eclipses today, I would have got nowhere without the material he has gathered – almost all of which can be downloaded from the Internet. I am equally in debt to my editor, Carol O'Brien, who has always stood by me, to my copy-editor, John Woodruff, whose encyclopaedic knowledge of astronomy saved me from many egregious errors and to Phil Whitaker for all his help with the Indian eclipse of 1995. Last but not least I am grateful to Maarten and yourself, and Carolien, your mother, for putting up with a *pater familias* whose presence was often eclipsed by his preoccupation with writing this book.

Finally, in a letter to a student of classics, I would like to suggest that you also look at the phenomenon of the solar eclipse *sub specie aeternatis*. On 11 August 1999 you will be, according to my demographic research, one of about 70,000 people worldwide who will not only be able to observe something of the eclipse, but will also be celebrating their twenty-first birthday. Of these 70,000, a little more than 2,000 will be somewhere in the United Kingdom, and well over 10 per cent of these will join the throngs enjoying the experience of totality in Cornwall and Devon. My guess is that you will be the only one of these with a father who has written a book focused on the conjunction of the eclipse of the Sun with a twenty-first birthday. I am delighted, therefore, that this conjunction provides the opportunity of dedicating this book to you. But I should like you also to remember, first, the other 70,000 born on the same day as yourself, and living somewhere along the path of totality (noting that few of them are so well favoured by fortune), and second, that the eclipse of 11 August 1999, although perhaps visible to more people than any other in the course of history, is but one in a series that began long before *Homo sapiens sapiens* was first around, and will continue into the indefinite future, without requiring the continued presence of human observers (whose own future is much more problematic). My book, therefore, is not just about 1999, the last year of the second millennium of what we are now taught to call the 'common era', but about all the millennia that went before and will come after it.

With all my love,

Thomas

Warning
11 August 1999 – viewing and photographing the eclipse

For the millions, in England and elsewhere, who will observe the solar eclipse of 11 August 1999, the period of partiality will last for two hours or more: although there will be much to be seen during this period, serious damage can be caused to the eyes by looking at the eclipsed sun without special protection. Ordinary sun-glasses will not be sufficient. For safe viewing, a mylar eclipse viewer is essential: this is no more than a cheap pair of spectacles with mylar instead of glass. Layers of exposed dark X-ray or other camera film may provide equal protection, but mylar viewers are certain to be widely available as the day of the eclipse approaches.

During the minute or two of totality, the sky, including the eclipsed sun, can safely be viewed with the naked eye, but *only* after the last limb of the sun has disappeared from sight. During this period cameras can be used, without special filters, to photograph the eclipse, although a telephoto lens is to be recommended. Once again, outside totality, the light is too brilliant for photographing the eclipsed sun, unless special purpose-built filters are used. Ordinary day-light filters are not sufficient.

1

The Eclipse as Phenomenon

The phænomenon [of a total eclipse of the sun]
in fact is one of the most terrible that man can
witness, and no degree of partial eclipses gives
any idea of its horror.

GEORGE BIDDELL, Astronomer Royal, in 1853[1]

The hidden Sun

Darkness at Noon, the title of a well-known book by Arthur
Koestler, not only evokes the impact of the Sun disappearing
from sight in the middle of the day, but also refers back to
St Matthew's gospel which tells us that 'from the sixth hour
there was darkness over all the land until the ninth hour'.[2]
In the gospel narrative these were the three afternoon hours
that Christ spent upon the cross, which many Christians
would claim were the most dramatic hours in the history of
the world. In the order of the cosmos, the experience
described by St Matthew could have only one cause: the
Moon coming between the Earth and the Sun. This is the
solar eclipse, which deprives humankind, for hardly more
than an instant, of the light of the Sun.

As a phenomenon, an eclipse of the Sun can be described
in two ways. The first way is subjective, and takes into
account the reactions of observers, conditioned by their own

15

cultural inheritance. Such reactions provide the leitmotiv of the present chapter. The perspective, therefore, is partly psychological. The second way is objective: observers are detached, so that they can describe the event independently of their own feelings. This may make almost superhuman demands upon the observer, but none the less provides the only acceptable starting point for describing the phenomenon scientifically.

For observers at any given point, the eclipse of the Sun does not occur suddenly. From the moment of what is misleadingly called *first contact*, when the Sun and the Moon (which are in fact separated by a distance of some 150,000,000 km) first overlap, the Moon takes an hour or more to pass across the Sun. The time of first contact depends on the path of the Moon's shadow as it races across the surface of the Earth, and varies from one location to another along the path. So long as the Moon does not hide the whole of the Sun, the eclipse is no more than partial; this is so for most of the two hundred or more solar eclipses occurring in the course of a century. A partial eclipse continues, after first contact, with a period of steadily increasing darkness until the point is reached where the degree of overlap is greatest. As the Moon moves on, daylight is restored at the same rate as observers had first been deprived of it. For reasons that will become clear, the eclipse ends with *fourth contact*, which defines the moment at which the Moon no longer hides any part of the Sun. In a partial eclipse the part of the Sun hidden by the Moon always falls short of 100 per cent. The maximum actually attained, say 90 per cent, defines a path across the Earth's surface along which the darkness of the Moon's shadow will be of maximum intensity. In a broad band either side of this path the eclipse will still be experienced, but at a lesser intensity. Where partiality comes near to 100 per cent, such a band may cover, in the two to three hours of the eclipse, a large part of the

16

Earth's surface, but away from the central path the phenomenon may be experienced as no more than a dull day and towards the edges there is little perceptible change in light intensity.

For over a quarter of all eclipses occurring in the course of time, the Moon, as it passes across the Sun, reaches a point at which it hides the Sun completely from observers in a small area completely under the shadow of the Moon – which itself moves rapidly across the surface of the Earth, like the shadow of a cloud on a windy day (although the actual speed of the Moon, relative to the Earth, is 3,200 kph). This happens about seven times in any decade. The point at which the partial eclipse then becomes total is the so-called *second contact* (where once again the Moon comes nowhere near to actually 'touching' the Sun). It may seem obvious, but this can happen only if the apparent size of the Moon, as seen from the Earth, is greater than that of the Sun. The relative sizes of the Moon and the Sun, as seen by an observer, define the magnitude of a total eclipse (which thus determines the relative positions of the Sun, the Earth and the Moon in their respective orbits at the time of an eclipse). The magnitude varies within very small margins either side of 1. The difference is critical, for with a magnitude less than 1, by however small an amount, the eclipse will not be total (it will be *annular* – see Chapter 2).

In a total eclipse the Moon casts an elliptical shadow, usually a few hundred kilometres wide, onto the Earth's surface. The shadow traces out a path across the surface, taking up to three hours to do so; each point on the path experiences totality for just a few minutes. Totality (which began with *second contact*) ends with *third contact*, when a limb of the Sun once more appears from behind the Moon. Outside the path of totality there is no second or third contact, and the eclipse, no more than partial, proceeds from first to fourth contact, the level of darkness first increasing and then decreasing in the way already described. Observers across a great part of the Earth's surface will share the experience, once again at different levels of light intensity depending upon their distance from the path of totality. Essentially the experience is no different from that of the majority of solar eclipses that never achieve totality.

Within the narrow path of totality the experience is quite different, and much more dramatic. As the Moon completely hides the Sun, the whole landscape quickly becomes as dark as it is on any normal day some forty minutes after sunset. The intensity of light falls to about 1/100,000th of its usual daytime level. This is the experience of the total eclipse, with the Sun completely hidden by the Moon during the period between second contact (when the sun finally disappears) and third contact (when it first reappears). It never lasts as long as eight minutes, and with the solar eclipse of 11 August 1999 – the first to be total anywhere in the United Kingdom since 1927 – it will last hardly more than two. With third contact the eclipse becomes partial, and continues as such to end at fourth contact.

To avoid confusion about this denouement, it is useful to

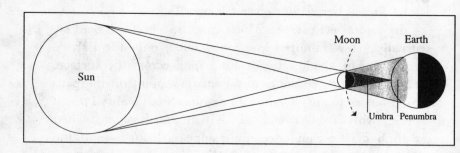

Figure 1.1 The umbra and penumbra of the Moon's shadow during a solar eclipse.

recapitulate the different ways in which an eclipse can be partial. First, the majority of solar eclipses are never more than partial, simply because during the eclipse no part of the Earth falls under the moon's dark inner shadow, or *umbra*. Because the Moon, as it passes across the Sun, never deprives the Earth of the whole of the Sun's light, that part of the surface of the Earth subject to the eclipse falls under the outer shadow, the *penumbra*. Second, even when a small part of the Earth's surface does come to fall within the *umbra* (and thus experiences a total eclipse), there will be a much larger area surrounding it which is within the *penumbra*, as shown in Figure 1.1; once again, some of the Sun's light still reaches the Earth. In this second case, the eclipse is never more than partial outside the path of totality, and even within the path it is still partial between first and second contact, and between third and fourth contact. Inevitably, then, totality, whenever it occurs, is always the climax to an experience which begins and ends with partiality: this is represented graphically by Figure 1.2 (from which it should be noted that the two periods of partiality account for more than 90 per cent of the duration of the eclipse).

Across Europe the path of totality of the 1999 eclipse will be just over 100 km wide, so the elliptical area in darkness at any one time will never quite reach 9,000 square kilometres. To observers on the ground it will not be immediately apparent that the shadow of the Moon is actually racing across the surface of the Earth, so that the experience of totality will be shared, within a matter of hours, by people living thousands of kilometres away. For England the area for which the eclipse will be total is about two and a half times that of Cornwall, but as the eclipse crosses the county, most of the area experiencing totality will be not land, but the surrounding sea. North-east of Cornwall will be outside the path of totality, while only south-west Devon will be within it. After that the path crosses the English Channel

19

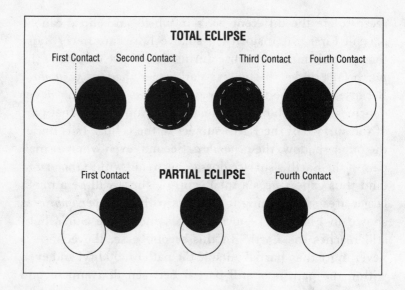

Figure 1.2 Contacts in total and partial eclipses.

to northern France, where far more people are likely to experience totality than in England.

Totality lasts longest at the centre-line of the path: in Cornwall this will be just over two minutes. Totality will last for about some 45 seconds when the Sun rises over the Atlantic some 300 km east of Cape Cod, and its dimensions, in both time and space, will steadily increase up to the point of greatest eclipse, close to the city of Rîmnicu-Vîlcea in the middle of Romania. Beyond this point the dimensions will decrease steadily until the local sunset brings an end to the eclipse, in the Bay of Bengal, just to the east of India; at this point totality will also last for about 45 seconds. At both the start and end points, off Cape Cod and India, the width of the path of totality (which varies according to the duration in time of totality) will be some 60 km. Nothing, however, prevents the Sun from being totally eclipsed by the Moon at the moment either of rising or setting. This is not abnormal, and the fact that it will happen with the 1999 eclipse is not particularly significant.

The modern eclipse experience

Totality is both the climax to a solar eclipse, and a significant change in the phenomenon itself. Until just before second contact the features of the landscape are clearly visible and well defined, but then suddenly it is nightfall. The considerable reduction in light intensity with the onset of totality (as already noted, by a factor of 100,000) is illustrated in Figure 1.3. This demonstrates the truth of the words of a mid-nineteenth-century Astronomer Royal quoted at the head of this chapter. The fact that a professional astronomer used the word 'terrible' at a time when the celestial dynamics of eclipses held few secrets makes it clear how immense the experience of totality can be.

The actual transition from a partial to a total eclipse has been described many times; the earliest complete records go back nearly three thousand years. The weather – always an uncertain factor when it comes to witnessing an eclipse – will decide just how impressive the phenomenon will be. When partiality approaches 100 per cent, fine weather may allow observers in a locality with trees to see on the ground myriad images of the crescent Sun as its light shines through the foliage. Within the path of totality this will be no more than a prelude to an even greater drama. Particularly in the south of England where, even outside the path of totality, partiality will for a few minutes exceed 95 per cent, it will have to be a very bleak August day for the eclipse not to make a considerable impact – even for city dwellers deprived of trees.

Totality is altogether different. Whatever the weather, the natural world reacts as if night has fallen. An evocative

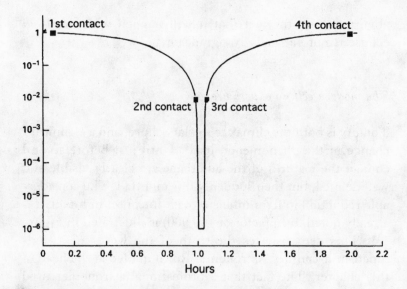

Figure 1.3 Total eclipse: changes in light intensity.

report, from the *Aberdeen Observer*, of the eclipse of 15 May 1836, describes how

> at an early stage if the eclipse, the wild birds ceased to sing, and they struck up their notes again very soon after the time of greatest obscuration. Sea-fowl were seen as flying at greater than ordinary elevation, striving as some thought, to find the cause of the unusual *crepusculum*; and in barn-yards the poultry were huddled together and chattering by turns, as if they had been engaged in deep consultation regarding the time of day.

As we shall find, as darkness descends on 11 August 1999, birds stop singing and go to roost, animals return to their lairs and flowers close up. The brighter stars and planets, and even the occasional comet, appear in the sky. The full visual impact of an eclipse demands fine weather if observers

22

on the ground are to witness all that happens to the Sun and the heavens around it. Totality can last at most seven and a half minutes – in 1999, 2 minutes 19.3 seconds will be the maximum – so the phenomena to be observed during the transition from a partial to a total eclipse take place in a very short time interval.

None the less, these phenomena are spectacular. To begin with, while a small crescent of the Sun is still visible, a pattern of alternating light and dark bands (known technically as 'shadow bands') can sometimes be seen rippling across any flat, light-coloured surface. Then, just as the crescent begins to disappear like the last traces of the smile on the face of the Cheshire cat (as described by Lewis Carroll in *Alice in Wonderland*), so that the Sun is covered by the dark face that the Moon presents to those observing the eclipse, a string of glittering points of light appears around it. These are *Baily's beads*, named after Francis Baily (1774– 1844), the amateur astronomer who first noted them. Lasting barely a quarter of a minute, Baily's beads are caused by the last of the Sun's rays finding their way between the mountains around the Moon's limb. The climax comes in the form of the so-called *diamond ring*, which lasts but an instant before totality sets in. This is caused by the last rays of sunlight shining through a valley on the Moon's limb, creating a single intense point of light. This is the 'diamond'; the 'ring' is the faint glow of light seen around the Moon's limb at this time.

A distant horizon may be outside the limits of totality, and so retain some brightness, demonstrating how a solar eclipse is always a local phenomenon. The sea, with its distant, level horizon, provides the best opportunities for observing this effect. This is unlike anything seen in the minutes following an ordinary sunset. The unearthly effect is, however, as nothing compared to the appearance of the Sun's corona, which can be seen only during a solar eclipse.

23

The corona, consisting of ionized gases, is the turbulent outer atmosphere of the Sun which extends into space for several times the Sun's diameter. During totality that part of it close to the Sun is visible to the naked eye. The appearance of the corona is the eclipse phenomenon of most interest to solar physics.[3] Totality ends at third contact, when the diamond ring may reappear, and Baily's beads are seen again.

With fourth contact the eclipse is over – at least as a local phenomenon. Those who cannot bear to lose it must follow its course in some supersonic flight, such as that of the Concorde which accompanied the shadow of the Moon in its journey across the Sahara during the eclipse of 30 June 1973. Those who remain on the ground will see how all living things resume their normal course; for them a few minutes of darkness will have changed next to nothing.

Human reactions

Where nature is largely free from mental trauma, the opposite is the case with humankind. Not only does the experience of an eclipse make an indelible impression upon all those who share it, but humans, with their remarkable and unique gift of speech and language, can communicate it to others of their kind. Although the great eclipse of 1999 will occur a month before my seventieth birthday, it will be the first total eclipse I will ever have witnessed. Everything I have outlined above has been communicated to me, mostly through the written word, by others, and not all of them have experienced a total solar eclipse. It is more than likely that professional colleagues such as Frédéric Clette in Belgium and Fred Espenak in the United States are the only people I know who have actually observed totality. Even so, the almost unlimited power we now have to communicate

across both time and space allows me to describe in considerable detail an event which has yet to take place: the only
uncertainty is the weather, and even this contingency can
be contained by the resources of modern technology.

Plymouth Hoe, although not quite on the centre-line of
the path of totality, offers everything for optimal observation.
The Hoe contains a considerable flat area, facing south and
overlooking the sea, so that with good weather some at least
of the 200,000 visitors expected in Plymouth on the day will
be able to observe the eclipse to maximum advantage. The
city, however, is taking no chances. If the weather is poor,
giant television screens placed at strategic points on the Hoe
will show the eclipse as it is observed by a specially equipped
aircraft flying above the clouds, and circling the city.

The perspective on the eclipse presented above belongs
entirely to the modern age: it is the product of a completely
literate society with unlimited access to the media. The path
of the 1999 eclipse will cross a remarkable area of land rather
than sea, to be experienced by more people than any eclipse
occurring during the whole history of humankind (see Chapter 8). The most remarkable thing about this day, seen from
that long-term perspective, is that the experience will have
been anticipated in one way or another by almost all who
will share it. The path of totality, extending from the south-
west of England to the east of India, will pass over many
different lands. No one would suggest that the cultures of,
say, Luxembourg, Hungary, Turkey, Iran and India are
homogeneous, and the question of cultural diversity in the
context of the expected eclipse cannot simply be disregarded.
None the less, an anthropologist would be hard put to find
any local population, however small, along the line of totality
which on 10 August 1999 did not anticipate in some sense,
however ill-informed, the unique event of the following day.
(Oddly enough, this may not have been true of the eclipse
of 26 February 1998, when the path of totality crossed the

25

frontier area between Colombia and Panama. In this inaccessible area, which contains the only gap in the Inter-American Highway between Alaska and Chile, there may still be one or two native American tribes who would have known nothing beforehand of what would overcome them that day.)

Let us in our minds return to a world ignorant of the celestial dynamics of eclipses. It is the gift of speech that makes man 'uniquely human',[4] and we as humans have been able to talk with one another for a period measured in tens of thousands of years. Not only all human thought, but memory also, is cast in terms of language, and it is our capacity to remember that enables us to establish and maintain a cultural resource capable of existing far longer than the life-span of any one of us. This resource is known by a number of names, such as *folklore* or *oral tradition*, which emphasise different aspects of it. But however diligent and inventive the individuals that make use of it are in preserving it, it still has its limitations.

When it comes to incorporating the phenomenon of the solar eclipse into any traditional culture, these limitations are absolutely critical. If we could go back just ten thousand years (which is a relatively short period in the history of *Homo sapiens sapiens*), we would find small isolated groups, each going its own way with little contact with outsiders, living in a world whose total population was about one five-hundredth of what it is today. There was more than enough room for everyone, and if two groups came into contact they would find their languages were mutually incomprehensible, so that there was little chance of their sharing any cultural resource that depended upon memory and oral communication.

In the prehistory of *Homo sapiens sapiens* (which means the first hundred thousand years) any number of such groups must have experienced a solar eclipse, but there is no way we can ever find any record of how they reacted to it. One thing is certain: for those observing the phenomenon it was a one-off, with no known precedent, and it would have been next to impossible for them to relate it to anything in their own experience. Finding an explanation would have been extremely problematic. (The rare cases in which a given locality experiences two eclipses within a period of a few years provide the only possible exception.) The light of the Sun was shut off in the middle of the day, but why should this happen when it had never happened before? Above all, what was the hidden meaning of this 'terrible' phenomenon? And what language could be used to describe it?

A comprehensive answer to this question must wait until Chapter 9, but at this stage it requires some qualification. Over the short term (which here means anything less than, say, ten generations) the local occurrence of eclipses is quite arbitrary. Taking the eclipse of 11 August 1999, as it will be experienced in England, the last time that Falmouth – well within the path of totality this time round – was in this position was on 2 May 1715. The period of 284 years between 1715 and 1999 is rather less than the average time, 375 years, between two successive instances of totality at any one place. Going back to the world of ten thousand years (and more) ago, this is too long for any but the vaguest folk memory. On the other hand, if we return to the eclipse of 1715 we find that in the south-west of England and Wales the path of totality was crossed, nine years later, by that of another eclipse, also in the month of May.

It is a reasonable conjecture, then, that the people of South Wales, and most of England south and west of London, who experienced both the eclipse of the 2 May 1715 and that of 22 May 1724,[5] must have had, on the second occasion, a distinct sense of *déja vu*. Some, at least, on both occasions, must have been forewarned, for the advance prediction of eclipses was already well established in the seventeenth century. On the other hand, country people in and around Taunton in Somerset, near the point where the two centre-lines crossed, lived their lives, in those days before mass literacy, in a world which was both literally and metaphorically parochial (as it would remain until the days of Thomas Hardy's novels, getting on for two centuries later). The point, in any case, is simple enough. When the second eclipse occurred within ten years, any number of people must have had the experience of surviving the first one; it would be interesting to know what conclusions they came to following the repeat performance. Had the first eclipse (of 1715) taught them that such an event had no significant consequences – favourable or unfavourable – or did they, at the second eclipse (of 1722), feel that they had to react in the same way that they did with the first? As an anthropologist, I see this second alternative as the more likely scenario.

Ten years is a relatively long period compared to what Split (in modern Croatia) experienced in the thirteenth century, when the total eclipse on 3 June 1239 was followed by another on 6 October 1241. (But the world had moved on a bit between thirteenth-century Split and eighteenth-century Taunton.) In the twentieth century, Port Moresby, the capital of New Guinea (an island unknown to the Western world in the thirteenth century) experienced totality on 11 June 1983 and again on 22 November 1984. In fact, the path of totality for almost any eclipse will cross, somewhere along the line, the path of another occurring shortly before or after. To take the 1999 eclipse, two areas along the path of totality, one around the Turkish city of Erzincan, and the other around the Indian city of Ahmedabad, will within ten years experience another solar eclipse: at Erzincan on 29 March 2006, and at Ahmedabad on 22 July 2009. Just how people in Turkey or India will react to this double whammy cannot now be predicted, but react they certainly will.

Eclipses in time and space

All these isolated incidents can be properly understood only by placing them in a cosmic frame. We now know that the paths of the Earth and the Moon in their established orbits ensure the constant, predictable and regular occurrence of both solar and lunar eclipses. As to the former, in an average century there are 238 solar eclipses, but of these only 66 ever achieve totality, so that total eclipses occur about twice every three years (as is confirmed by the seven instances, ending with 11 August 1999, in the 1990s). The paths of totality, for different eclipses, not only cross every part of the world, but they also cross one another. Since their distribution is more or less random in the short term (meaning less than, say, ten thousand years), two paths will occasionally intersect within a very short time – sometimes no longer than the period between two successive total eclipses. The principle is the same as the same number coming up twice running in roulette (which does not affect the general principle that any one number occurs on average once every 37 spins of the wheel).

In fact, for any given location the average period between two total successive solar eclipses is 375 years. Given that there are 66 such eclipses in a century, this means that with any one of them the chance of any given location experiencing totality, is about one in 250: this means that a path of totality, on *average* – a very loaded word in this context – covers 1/250 of the Earth's surface.

Fundamental properties

Finally, in a purely rational world there are three conclusions to be drawn from the observation of an eclipse, however deficient the understanding of the celestial dynamics. The

29

first is simply that the phenomenon can arise only because the Sun and Moon, as seen from the Earth, appear to be nearly the same size. In more technical language, they subtend nearly the same angle on the retina of the observer. In the cosmic order this is a massive coincidence.

The second conclusion is that, whatever rules govern the occurrence of an eclipse, the event, as experienced over its duration (which from first to fourth contact is never much longer than two hours), is symmetrical in time. In other words, the build-up between first and second contact is mirrored in the climb-down between third and fourth contact. Although this is true in principle, for the observer on the ground the description is 100 per cent accurate only when totality happens precisely at noon, local time (which is not often). Also, local sunrise, rather than first contact, may determine the time at which partiality is at first apparent, and similarly for local sunset and fourth contact. In such cases, at the first or last moment at which the eclipse can be observed the Sun is hidden, at least in part, by the Moon. We have already seen how both cases will apply to the eclipse of 11 August 1999.

This symmetry in the dimension of time has one important consequence for humankind, if not for any other natural species. Any effort, whether it be waving flags or beating drums, made to bring about the end of an eclipse is bound to be successful. The holy man who says, 'do this, or do that, and this terrible happening will cease' utters what appears to be a self-fulfilling prophecy. He also reaffirms a doom-laden view of the phenomenon that will keep him in business.

The third conclusion is that the eclipse changes next to nothing in the natural world: as the skies return to normal, birds start to sing, animals come out of their lairs and flowers open up. An eclipse, inexorable in the operation of the cosmos, is no trauma for the rest of nature, but it can be for

30

humankind: our minds are so plastic, our imaginations so fertile and our sense of disaster so acute, that we are inclined to read too much into so unprecedented an event. The result is to see it as a portent, and associate it with any untoward happening in the days or months that follow it. A king may die, the harvest may fail, storm and flood may devastate the land: in these cases, and many others, the eclipse could have been seen, if not as the cause then at least as a warning that should have been heeded. In our postmodern age all this is grist to the mill for the cognitive psychologist, but in times past it was a much more serious matter.

Lunar eclipses

In the premodern age, placing a solar eclipse in the general scheme of things was always problematic simply because there was so little to go by. Things were quite different, however, with lunar eclipses (which may be seen as a converse case). If the Moon can hide the Sun from the Earth, so too can the Earth hide the Sun from the Moon. The two cases, in principle, must go hand in hand in any eclipse month, with the solar eclipse occurring between two lunar cycles (one new Moon to the next), and the lunar eclipse in the middle of the cycle, at the time of full Moon.

The rule of symmetry cannot, however, be carried too far. Seen from the Moon the Earth appears much larger than the Sun, so that when its shadow covers the Moon, in a lunar eclipse, the whole Moon is hidden for more than an hour, and the phenomenon can be observed in the night sky from any part of the Earth then in darkness. This allows a lunar eclipse to be observed by the inhabitants of up to half the Earth's surface. This means that none of us need wait very long before having an opportunity to observe the phenomenon (although to do so we may have to get up in the small hours). In the quarter century for which I have lived in Amsterdam I have often witnessed a lunar eclipse from the street outside my front door, though sometimes poor weather, or reluctance to let my night's sleep be disturbed, have meant that I missed the opportunity. This latter factor, in the days before electric light, when country dwellers retired at dusk and got up at dawn, meant that lunar eclipses – without any forewarning from the media – often went unobserved save by a few night-owls (including, probably, agricultural labourers at the time of the harvest Moon) and professional astronomers. None the less, for those who cared to be up and about, they were seen to occur, like solar eclipses, several times in any decade (although none will now occur until after the beginning of the new millennium).

The phenomenon is, in any case, much less spectacular than a solar eclipse. The light of the Moon (as of any planet in the solar system) is no more than a pale reflection of that of the Sun, so that the loss of illumination caused by its temporary eclipse by the Earth, although still considerable, is much less striking. Subjectively, however, familiarity with lunar eclipses much often have gone some way to alleviate the terrible strangeness of solar eclipses. After all, as we shall see in the next chapter, the two phenomena both arise from the alignment of the three heavenly bodies that dominate our lives: the Sun, the Earth and the Moon.

2

The Celestial Dynamics of Eclipses

Occultation, Eclipse, Transit

It takes two to tango, but three to make an eclipse. An eclipse is the result of the alignment of three heavenly bodies in which one is a source of light, and the second prevents that light, wholly or partly, from reaching the third. As such it's a special case of two more general phenomena, occultation and transit. With occultation, the second of the three bodies is so large that it completely hides the third. Transit is the opposite case: the second body is so small that, as observed from the third, it appears to do no more than cross the source of light, like a fly buzzing round an electric light bulb.

A lunar eclipse is, essentially, a simple case of occultation. The mean distance of the Moon from the Earth, 384,410 km, is so small in relation to that of the Earth from the Sun, 149,597,900 km, that the Earth, with a diameter more than three times that of the Moon, is sufficiently large to cast a shadow which, at the distance of the Moon, has a diameter more than twice that of the Moon. The shadow would be much larger but for the fact that the Sun's diameter is more than a hundred times that of the Earth's. Even so – in spite of the fact that it is necessarily out of scale – the Moon is completely engulfed in the Earth's shadow. This allows for a period of totality lasting well over an hour, in sharp contrast to the few minutes, at most, of totality in a solar eclipse.

A solar eclipse may be thought of as an extreme example of a transit. If the Moon were smaller, or its mean distance from the Earth greater, then during alignment it would appear to transit the Sun, and in doing so would cast no dark shadow, or *umbra*, onto the Earth's surface. In this case (which, as we shall see, does actually occur) the point of the Moon's shadow cone would be a few thousand kilometres above the Earth's surface. The axis of the cone would still intersect the Earth, which would be within the Moon's lighter, outer shadow, the *penumbra*. The eclipse would never be more than partial. The difference between *umbra* and *penumbra* (which is critical for determining whether an eclipse ever becomes total) has already been illustrated in Figure 1.1.

The question remains, what principles of celestial dynamics ensure the regular alignment of the Sun, the Moon and the Earth, so that eclipses occur in the way that is recorded in the history of astronomy? Before we can answer this, we must take a synoptic view of the whole Solar System, considering its origins some four to five billion years ago.[1]

The Solar System

The Solar System comprises the Sun and everything held in orbit around it by its gravitational field. The Sun itself not only accounts for 99.86 per cent of the mass of the Solar System, but is also its central source of energy, so that the light of almost everything that can be seen in the Solar System comes from the Sun.

Next to the Sun, the major planets are the dominant components of the Solar System, and of these Jupiter accounts for two-thirds of their total mass. What is most remarkable about them is that, with the exception of the outermost planet, Pluto, their orbits all lie very nearly in the same plane, known as the plane of the *ecliptic*, defined by the Earth's orbit round the Sun. This is a result of the way that the planetary system of the Sun emerged as part of the process in which the Sun itself became a separate star within our Galaxy. This, known familiarly as the Milky Way, can be taken to be some three times as old as the Sun, and almost as old as the Universe – at least if one accepts the big bang theory of its creation.

The process by which a star forms, by the collapse of part of a cloud of gas and dust in the Galaxy, concentrates a vast store of energy at its centre (which manifests itself as the light of the star) but it also leaves a small residue of extra material in a vast flat disc. This material eventually coalesces, first as a result of electromagnetic forces and then by gravity, into a planetary system. The Solar System is the only such system open to exploration and close observation. As such it carries a heavy load as the sole representative of a phenomenon that, for all we know, is common throughout the Universe. This possibility was affirmed by the discovery from the mid-1990s of planet-sized objects orbiting some nearby stars. None the less, when it comes to eclipses, our Solar System is the only one we are concerned with.

The vast mass of the Sun in relation to that of the planets means that each of them can be considered as following their own elliptical orbit around the Sun, independently of the others. (Elliptical orbits were discovered by Johannes Kepler, who published the finding as his first law of planetary motion, at the beginning of the seventeenth century; the explanation of it came with Isaac Newton's law of gravity later in the same century.) The elliptical orbits represent what mathematicians call a 'first-order approximation', which means that they are sufficiently accurate for many practical purposes (and open to correction by further orders of approximation when observation and theory require this, for example to account for the small gravitational perturbations exerted by the planets on one another). In fact, the eccentricity of these orbits – the degree to which the ellipses they trace out depart from circles – is small. The actual measure of eccentricity is an index, which for the Earth is 0.017, and for Venus 0.007 – making its orbit the most circular of all the major planets. Pluto is quite exceptional with an eccentricity of 0.248, which means not only that there are considerable variations in its distance from the Sun, but also – given its mean distance from the Sun – that its orbit sometimes passes within that of Neptune.

For the dynamics of eclipses, what matters is the eccentricity not only of the Earth's orbit, but also that of the Moon's orbit round the Earth, which is much greater. The Moon is only one of many satellites of planets in the Solar System (although it is in fact the largest of them in relation to the planet it orbits[2]). Until the end of the sixteenth century (when only the five planets visible to the naked eye, Mercury, Venus, Mars, Jupiter and Saturn, were known), no one realised that all planets except the two, Mercury and Venus, inside the Earth's orbit, had moons. The invention of the telescope enabled Galileo, in 1609, to discover the four largest moons of Jupiter. (It is now known that Jupiter has at least 16 moons, and others may yet await discovery.) For our purposes it does not matter how moons were created in the course of the formation of the Solar System, but the existence of *our* moon has profoundly influenced the way humankind has perceived and interpreted the Universe.

The Moon (meaning our moon) has three notable properties – observable, if not correctly understood, throughout the history of humankind. The first, already noted in Chapter 1, is that, as seen by an observer at any point on the Earth, its size (which is larger than that of most other moons in the Solar System) is almost exactly the same as that of the Sun. The second is that the plane of the Moon's orbit is inclined at an angle, on average 5° 8',[3] to the plane of the ecliptic. The third is that it always shows the same face to us (which means that it rotates on its own axis in the same time that it takes to orbit the Earth). For the phenomenon of an eclipse, this third property is quite unimportant. The first two, however, are critical.

To complete this outline of the Solar System, and its place in the Universe, it is first to be noted that, in addition to the planets and their moons, there are countless other objects, mostly very small, hurtling round among the planets. Comets are the most spectacular, because they become visible as they approach the Sun. Around Easter 1997, Hale–Bopp, clearly visible for several weeks, aroused enormous popular interest. The few hundred comets which venture within the region of the planets originate in the Oort Cloud,[4] which lies far outside it. This contains trillions of comets and reaches about half-way to the nearest star: it is still part of the Solar System, and was probably formed from debris left over at the time of its formation.

Less impressive to the observer, but potentially much more terrifying in the long run, are asteroids – rocky bodies in orbit round the Sun. Although they are mostly very small compared with the planets and their largest moons – the biggest of them, Ceres, has a diameter of 933 km – asteroids are counted in millions. Fortunately the great majority are in orbit between Mars and Jupiter, safely out of harm's way as far as the Earth is concerned. The near-Earth asteroids are much smaller. None the less, the odd one does come our way, and one with a diameter of about 10 km, hitting the

Earth just off present-day Yucatán peninsula in Mexico some 65 million years ago, could account for the extinction of the dinosaurs (although some believe that the impact came from a comet). For a week or two at the beginning of 1998, it was thought that a large asteroid would come dangerously close to the Earth in October 2028, but then new calculations showed that it would miss us by a safe distance (which allows me to look forward to a restful 99th birthday in September 2028).

The Universe as background

Finally, there is the whole of the rest of the Universe, outside the Solar System. Looked at in terms of the galaxies which comprise it, and the countless stars – of many different kinds – contained in them, the Universe as a whole is neither uniform nor stable. The outer reaches of the Universe are of most interest to contemporary astrophysicists (who routinely study phenomena unknown a generation ago), but this is of little importance to eclipse astronomers (who still hold their own in the face of the host of astrophysicists). The usual frame of reference for the visible Universe is defined by the constellations and the stars they contain. Constellations are the basic 'territories' in the map of the celestial sphere as it is seen from any point on the Earth. The celestial sphere is the imaginary two-dimensional surface that appears to rotate on an axis whose poles correspond to the north and south poles of the Earth's axis. The rotation of the celestial sphere can be followed simply by observing the paths of the stars in the course of any night. The stars themselves appear to cluster in forms that evoked mythological figures in the minds of stargazers of ancient times. In the Western world these forms have constituted, for well over two thousand years, the constellations, with their familiar Latin names. In the ancient world these constellations were based on only those stars visible from the northern hemisphere – which include, none the less, several in the southern hemisphere of the celestial sphere.[5] In 1930, by which time both hemispheres were long known to astronomy, the International Astronomical Union agreed a definitive division of the celestial sphere into eighty-eight areas. This was no more than a logical extension of the constellations known to the ancient world. It preserved, for the most part, their original names, many of which are familiar to the wider public, particularly those of the twelve constellations comprising the Zodiac and featuring in astrological columns in popular newspapers.

Although what goes on outside the Solar System has little effect on eclipses of the Sun and Moon – which are essentially a phenomenon of planet Earth – the mapping of the heavens made possible by the system of constellations provides a frame of reference for locating eclipses. This is particularly useful when it comes to the historical record, since the exact position of the stars in the skies is known for any given time and place in recorded history. With our knowledge of the Saros (introduced on page 55), we can thus calculate, for any eclipse, the precise time and location (defined by appropriate coordinates on the celestial sphere) in one of the constellations of the Zodiac at which the Moon and the eclipsed Sun will lie. Figure 2.1 shows this location, in the boundary area between Leo and Cancer, at the moment at which Falmouth, in Cornwall, will lie at the centre of the path of totality on 11 August 1999. Because the Sun, in relation to the stars, moves relatively slowly – less than 1° per day – this location changes very little in the few hours that the eclipsed Sun follows its path across the heavens. Its direction, as seen by observers, changes much more rapidly, so that at Falmouth the eclipsed Sun will be in the south-east, whereas at the time of maximum eclipse, at Rîmnicu-Vîlcea in Romania, it will be just west of south.

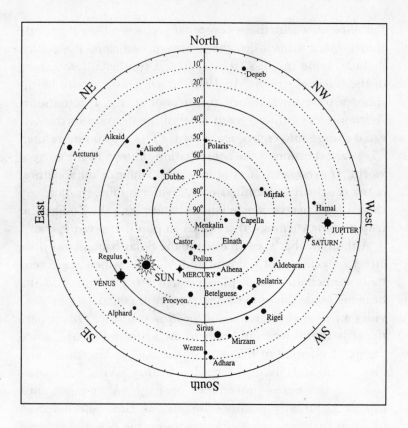

Figure 2.1 The sky as it will appear from Falmouth during totality on 11 August 1999.

Our exact knowledge of the path of totality extends, in principle, back to the time of the first recorded eclipses. But, as we shall see later, we then have to take into account geophysical changes, notably in the speed of the Earth's rotation (which until the present century was the only means of determining the length of the day).

Although the stars that can be seen in the night sky trace their own paths across it between sunset and sunrise, some disappearing below the horizon as the hours advance and

40

others appearing above it, their configuration in relation to one another is fixed[6] in the pattern of the constellations. The motion of the night sky is apparent only to an observer on a rotating body such as the Earth. Astronomy makes better sense if the sky is taken as fixed, its actual appearance at any time during the night, and at any time of year, being determined by the rotation of the Earth on its axis combined with its revolution in its orbit round the Sun.

It is misleading also to talk of the 'night sky': the globe of the heavens is as complete as the globe of the Earth, with 360° of longitude and 90° of latitude both above and below the ecliptic. But as half the Earth is in darkness at any one time, so also is only half the sky visible at any one time, and then only during the hours of darkness. The stars are of course still present during the daylight hours, but with their light unable to compete with that of the Sun, they cannot be seen. In fact, if the stars could be seen, the Sun would be seen to be moving *eastwards*[7] across the heavens, making a complete circuit once every year (which means that its progress in any one day will be comparatively small, about a degree). At a solar eclipse, the Sun no longer drowns out the starlight during the minutes of totality. The stars which then appear are out of season, so that in an extreme case an eclipse at midday in the middle of the summer reveals the night sky of midwinter, the Moon appearing in a typical winter constellation such as Orion.

The celestial sphere, which is an image of the heavens seen from the inside looking out, is two-dimensional, which is how the sky always appears to be at night. However convenient this picture is for the purpose of representation (it is what enables maps of the heavens to be made), it can be misleading since it creates a conceptual association between heavenly bodies which has no basis in reality. To take the case of the constellation, Centaurus, the distance from the Sun of its brightest star, Alpha Centauri, is one-hundredth that of the next brightest, Beta Centauri.[8] To the astrophysicist the two have nothing whatever to do with each other. It is only on a map of the heavens that they seem to be associated.

This lengthy preamble has established the frame of reference in which the bodies in the Solar System – the Sun, the planets and their moons, comets, asteroids and artificial space travellers – all trace their paths. To an observer on the Earth's surface the Sun and the Moon are the only conspicuous travellers in this space: the Sun, by its brilliance, hides from the observer's view the frame of reference defined by the stars, but its light provides another means of tracing its path across the sky. (The most elementary instrument is the *gnomon*,[9] an upright pointer whose shadow traces the path of the Sun.) The light of the Moon (which is no more than the reflected light of the Sun) is too faint to cast a useful shadow, but then the Moon's passage across the sky can be observed in relation to the constellations through which it passes. When, as happens from time to time, the Moon is visible during the daytime, the constellations are still present, but the light from the stars comprising them is too faint to be seen by the naked eye. This demonstrates that, next to the Sun, the Moon, as seen from the Earth, is much the brightest of all the heavenly objects. The reason for something we all know anyway is simply that the Moon is so much closer: Venus, the planet that comes closest, still never comes closer than 43,000,000 km, which is about a hundred times the distance of the Moon from the Earth. Venus, and the other planets visible to the naked eye, were detected not because of their brightness (they are about as bright as the brightest stars) but because their position in the night sky constantly changes in relation to that of the constellations which define it. It is not for nothing that the word 'planet' itself comes from the Greek for 'wanderer'.

How eclipses occur

The stage has now been set to discover how and when eclipses occur. Figure 2.2 shows both the Earth's orbit round the Sun and the Moon's orbit round the Earth. The moon

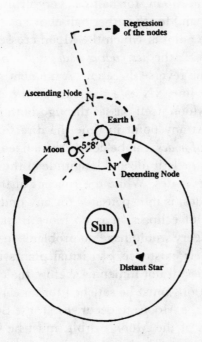

Figure 2.2 The orbits of the Earth and Moon.

is shown in a position where we see its phase as just past last quarter. The arrows indicate the direction of motion of the Earth and the Moon in their orbits (note that the Earth rotates on its axis in the same anticlockwise direction). The perspective taken for this diagram shows the north, rather than the south pole. There is nothing, in principle, against taking the view from 'below', which would mean simply that all the directions would be reversed. The fact that the historical record was established in the northern hemisphere explains the conventional view from 'above'.

The Moon's orbital plane is inclined to the plane of the ecliptic by 5° 8'. The two points N and N' at which the Moon's orbit intersects the plane of the ecliptic are called the nodes. The Moon, for half of every orbit, is below the ecliptic plane, and for the other half above it. N, the *ascending node* is the point at which the Moon crosses from below to above, and N', the *descending node*, is the point at which it crosses in the reverse direction. A moment's thought will show that the line NN' is a diameter of the Moon's orbit, and that the Moon itself passes through both nodes once in every cycle. At any point in time the direction of the line NN', the *line of nodes*, can be defined by a fixed star to which it points, and the latitude and longitude of the star will then define its coordinates. While the concept of the nodes, and the line of nodes, is indispensable for any understanding of the dynamics of eclipses, it is no more than that: today's computer imagery would have no problems in depicting the nodes, but their existence, as virtual points in space, was known centuries, if not millennia, before the computer age.

Two conditions must be satisfied for an eclipse (whether of the Sun or the Moon) to occur. First, the Sun, the Earth and the nodes of the Moon's orbit, must be in alignment; second, the Moon, at the instant of alignment, must be at one of its nodes. If in Figure 2.3, the line NN' passed through the sun, the Moon at N' would be between the Earth and the Sun and there would be a solar eclipse. If the Moon were at N, there would be a lunar eclipse. The fact that the Moon and the Earth have finite dimensions means that there is considerable leeway: there can still be an eclipse if the alignment of the nodes is not perfect, or if the Moon, in relation to the relevant node, is slightly off-centre. Since the Moon

44

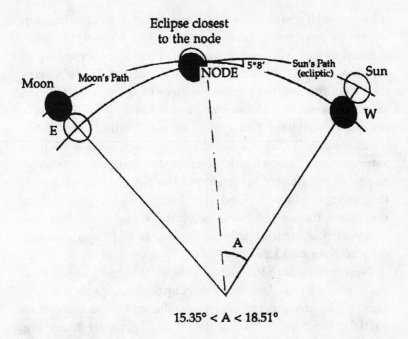

Figure 2.3 The ecliptic limits: the angular separations form the Moon's nodes within which eclipses can occur.

progresses from one node to the other in a period measured in days, lunar and solar eclipses occur in tandem, provided that the angle between the line of nodes and the line from the Earth to the Sun remains sufficiently close to zero – the angle of perfect alignment.

Since a partial eclipse occurs from the point in the Moon's orbit where the Sun and the Moon just touch (as shown in Figure 2.3), this point defines the greatest distance the Moon can be from a node for an eclipse to still occur. The measure, adopted by convention, is the maximum angle (A in Figure 2.4) by which the direction of the node from the Earth can deviate from that of the Sun and still produce an eclipse.

This in turn determines the number of eclipses that can occur in any given year. Confusingly, the *ecliptic limit*, defined in this way, is not constant, but varies according to two key factors: the actual inclination of the Moon's orbit to the ecliptic, and the apparent sizes of the Sun and Moon as they appear to an observer on the Earth. The first has a secular (long-term) variation of about 8' either side of the mean value of 5° 8' – a small perturbation long known to astronomers. The second factor is the result of the eccentricity of the Earth's orbit around the Sun, and, even more, that of the Moon around the Earth. These two factors together – the second being much more important than the first – define a major ecliptic limit of 18.51° and a minor ecliptic limit of 15.35°.

Needless to say, for a total eclipse to occur, the critical point must be well within the ecliptic limit (which is one reason why the great majority of eclipses are no more than partial); for totality the angle A in Figure 2.4 must not exceed 11.8°. Even so, this condition is not always sufficient, since at the time of an eclipse the distance of the Moon from the Earth can exceed the length of the Moon's *umbra*, in which case the Moon will not entirely hide the Sun. On such occasions a ring (or *annulus*) of sunlight is always visible round the Moon, so that the eclipse, at its maximum, is *annular* rather than total.[10] How, and why this happens, will be explained in the following section.

The line of nodes, NN', does not have a constant orientation in space: the line itself rotates, or *regresses*, once every 18.61 years. Since the line of nodes rotates in the opposite direction – whence the use of the word 'regression' – to that of the Earth and the Moon in their orbits, the alignment NN' with the Sun recurs after a period which is 18.62 days shorter than a solar year. This defines an *eclipse year* of 346.62 days. In any such year there will be two such alignments, NN' and N'N, each occurring at some stage in the course of a *synodic month*, defined as the interval between two successive new Moons, 29.53 days.[11] In this period of time, the Sun (taking into account the length of an eclipse year) moves 30.67° (29.53 days × 360°/346.62 days) across the sky. Since this distance is less than twice the minor ecliptic limit (15.35°), every synodic month in which an alignment, NN' or N'N, with the Sun occurs defines an *eclipse season* in which there must be at least one solar eclipse.

This is a very significant fact, for it establishes the basic rhythm of eclipses over the course of time. The margins are critical: if the angle between the plane of the Moon's orbit and that of the ecliptic were a little larger, then – as is clear from Figure 2.4 – the ecliptic limits would be smaller and eclipse seasons would occur without a solar eclipse. Indeed, the greater this angle, the less frequent eclipses would be. If the angle were 90° eclipses would never happen at all.[12] In the other direction, as the angle of the Moon's orbit tends to zero, the ecliptic limits widen, so that the eclipse season, at a certain point, would always contain two solar eclipses (which happens, very occasionally, within the present limits). If the Moon's orbit actually lay in the plane of the ecliptic, there would be a solar eclipse with every new Moon. As things are, the angle between the Moon's orbit and the ecliptic – varying between 5° 0' and 5° 16' – is such that the eclipse season advances a month every time a series of about nine eclipses is completed.

Eccentricity

As we have seen, eccentricity defines the degree to which the focus of an elliptical orbit is off-centre.[13] It therefore applies both to the Moon's orbit around the Earth, and to the Earth's orbit around the Sun. One focus of the elliptical orbit coincides with the centre of gravity of the two bodies concerned. Since the mass of the Sun is more than 300,000 times that of the Earth, in this case the point actually lies within the Sun, so that in practice, the Sun may be taken as the focus of the Earth's elliptical orbit. The same is true of the Moon in relation to the Earth, the centre of gravity (known in this case as the barycentre) lying about 1600 km below the Earth's surface. The eccentricity of the Moon's orbit around the Earth (0.066) is significantly greater than that of the Earth's orbit around the Sun (0.017). This means that the Moon's distance from the Earth is more important in determining the time and coordinates of an eclipse than is the Earth's distance from the Sun. So, for an observer on the Earth, eccentricity is important for defining, first, the distance of the Earth from the Sun, and second, that of the Moon from the Earth. These distances, together with the diameters of the Sun (1,392,530 km) and the Moon (3,476 km), determine their apparent sizes as seen from the Earth. The Table on p.49 gives both the mean and the limiting values of distances from the Earth and apparent sizes. The relation between these two factors is complex and requires further explanation. The Table shows that the range of apparent sizes is much greater for the Moon than for the Sun, the limits for the Moon exceeding those for the Sun at both maximum and minimum. On the other hand, the mean is slightly smaller for the Moon than for the Sun. Since a total eclipse requires the apparent size of the Moon to be greater than that of the Sun, there will be many occasions on which totality fails to occur simply because this is not the case. Then, instead of the Sun being totally hidden from observers in the short period between second and third contact, a narrow rim of sunlight will be visible around the Moon. This is the phenomenon of the annular eclipse.

Table 1. Distances and apparent sizes of the Sun and Moon.

	Minimum	Mean	Maximum
Distances from the Earth (km)			
Sun	147,000,000	149,600,000	152,000,000
Moon	356,400	384,400	406,700
Apparent sizes (minutes of arc)			
Sun	31.49	32.03	32.57
Moon	29.38	31.45	33.53

The dividing line between an annular and a total eclipse is evident from the ratio of the apparent size of the Moon to that of the Sun. Plainly, when this ratio is greater than 1 the eclipse is total, while for an annular eclipse the ratio must be less than 1. In the former case the Moon's shadow cone (which defines the umbra) reaches the earth; in the latter case it fails to do so, the point of the cone falling a relatively short distance from the Earth's surface. From the figures given in Table 1, it can be calculated that the ratio of apparent sizes can vary between 0.902 and 1.065.

The length of the Moon's shadow cone is a function only of its distance from the Sun: the greater the distance, the longer the shadow cone. Since, at the time of a solar eclipse, the Moon is between the Sun and the Earth, its distance from the Sun will then be the difference between its distance from the Earth and the Earth's distance from the Sun. Calculated in this way the mean distance is 149.2×10^6 km, which, given the diameter (3,476 km) of the Moon in relation to that (1,392,000 km) of the Sun, means that the mean length of the shadow cone is 373,000 km. Taking into account the eccentricity of the two orbits – of the Moon around the Earth and the Earth around the Sun – the actual length varies between 366,000 and 379,000 km.

When it comes to the Moon's distance from the Earth, this varies between 356,400 km at *perigee* (the point in its orbit closest to the Earth) and 406,700 km at *apogee* (the point farthest away), giving a much greater range than for the length of the shadow cone. Combining the figures in this and the preceding paragraph, it will be seen that when the distance of the Moon from the Earth is more than 379,000 km there is no possibility of a total eclipse occurring, whereas whenever it is less than 366,000 km any eclipse should have a period of totality (and therefore a magnitude greater than 1). In the middle range, when the Moon is less than 379,000 km but more than 366,000 km from the Earth, the possibility of totality depends upon its distance from the Sun (which is largely determined by that of the Earth from the Sun). When the eclipse is total, its magnitude will determine both the maximum extent of the area in which totality will be experienced, and the maximum time for which totality can then last. In fact the maximum area is some 57,000 km^2, and the maximum duration 7 minutes and 40 seconds, but an eclipse approaching these dimensions occurs very rarely, the last instance being that which crossed the Sahara in 1973. There is one final point: as shown by the above analysis, maximum duration requires the Moon to be at perigee. Kepler's second law (as stated on page 105) then requires that the angular speed of the Moon is at its maximum. This means that it moves faster across the sky in relation to the Sun, and thus actually reduces the duration of every phase of the eclipse, including totality.

The gamma factor

We are not yet quite out of the woods, for we still need to look in detail at the way in which any eclipse actually impacts upon the earth. We need to ask what factors determine the degree to which an eclipse deprives any location on Earth of the light of the Sun. These factors divide into two classes: the first, defined by the location of the Moon between the two ecliptic limits, is dealt with in this section. The second, defined by local time, is dealt with in the following section, 'The Earth's rotation'.

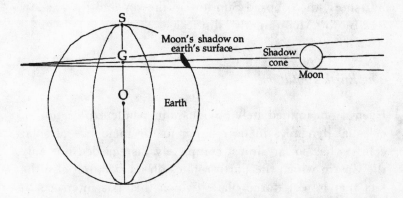

Figure 2.4 The Moon's shadow cone, and the shadow cast on the Earth. The ratio OG/OS defines the quantity γ.

For every solar eclipse there is a minimum distance between the axis of the Moon's shadow cone and the centre of the Earth. The ratio of this distance to that of the Earth's radius at the equator (6,378 km) is known as γ (gamma). The principle is illustrated in Figure 2.4, where $\gamma = OG/OS$. By convention, γ is positive north of the equator, and negative south of it. Because of the flattening of the Earth, for totality to occur γ must fall between the limits ±0.997. Where the distances separating the Earth from the Moon and from the Sun rule out totality, the same principles apply to the annular eclipse which may then occur. The important point is that γ, next to the magnitude, is the simplest measure of the character of any eclipse.[14] A low absolute value for γ characterises an eclipse with a long, relatively narrow path and a near-circular shadow. The path is longest and narrowest when the eclipsed Sun is directly overhead, which can occur only in the tropics, for then $\gamma = 0$; although theoretically possible, this seldom occurs in practice. At the other extreme, characteristic of high latitudes, when γ comes close to its greatest value, the path of totality will be broad but short, the eclipsed Sun low in the sky and the shadow cast by the Moon highly elliptical.

The Earth's rotation

Even if not immediately obvious, our whole exploration of celestial dynamics in its relation to the incidence of solar eclipses has so far almost completely disregarded not only the way in which the Earth rotates on its axis, but also the fact that its equatorial plane (which this axis intersects at right angles) is inclined to the ecliptic at an angle of 23° 27'. Such disregard is not perverse, but quite deliberate. To an observer located at some arbitrary point in the Solar System, the extent and duration of an eclipse would not depend on the geographical limits of the area on Earth from which the eclipse is observable. Such an observer could note the phenomenon of a solar eclipse (and write most of this chapter) without even having discovered the Earth's rotation. Needless to say, for the Earth-bound observer these geographical limits are critical – and historically they provide the starting point for the systematic study of solar eclipses. The truth of this statement will become more apparent in Chapter 5. An examination of the most ancient recorded eclipses shows that they did not occur, geographically, in locations determined according to the principles of celestial dynamics considered in this chapter. According to these principles, these eclipses occurred in the wrong place, but still the

52

historical records cannot be gainsaid. Everything else about these eclipses was right. Now it is sufficient to note that the reasons for the discrepancy lie in the realm of geophysics, which this chapter has ignored.

The correct principle, at the present stage, is that the laws of celestial dynamics are completely sufficient to establish all the dimensions of an eclipse in time and space. If the Earth (like the Moon in relation to the Earth) presented only one face to the Sun, the time dimension would play little part in determining the geographical location of an eclipse. Since, however, the Earth makes up to about a sixth of a rotation during the time of an eclipse, this is a major factor in determining which parts of the Earth's surface actually experience it. The eclipse of 11 August 1999 will last just over three hours from start to finish, during which time the Earth will rotate through an angle of 46°. In terms of longitude, however, the length of the path of totality, extending from 65°W to 86°E, will be 151° – equivalent to 42 per cent of a rotation of the Earth.

The flattened Earth and the perturbed Moon

The Earth is not a perfect sphere, but is flattened at the poles in such a way that the distance between the north and south poles is less than the Earth's diameter at the equator, by a factor of 1/298.25. This affects the incidence of solar eclipses in two ways, one simple and the other rather complicated. The simple way is that the angle (A in Figure 2.4) between the two extreme positions for an eclipse to occur in the polar regions is smaller than it would be if the Earth were a perfect sphere. In practice this means that some polar eclipses are no more than partial when otherwise they would have a period of totality, with a corresponding reduction in the magnitude.

The complicated way has to do with two phenomena known as *precession* and *nutation*. Precession was discovered by Hipparchus in the second century BC, but it was explained by Isaac Newton some eighteen centuries later. The phenomenon is simple enough. On the celestial sphere lies a circle, the celestial equator, which is always in the same plane as the Earth's equator. Given that the Earth revolves around the Sun in the plane of the ecliptic (which is close to the orbital planes of all the planets except for Pluto), then at the end of every complete circuit defined by reference to a fixed point, the configuration of the stars, as seen by any observer, should be precisely the same as it was at the beginning of the circuit. In short, at any given instant in the year the heavens, when observed from a given point on the Earth, should always appear to be exactly the same as they were at the corresponding instant a year earlier. Hipparchus discovered that this was not so. Instead, the fixed point of reference (by convention, the vernal equinox[15]) moved backwards along the ecliptic, but at a rate so slow that it takes 25,800 years to complete the 360° circuit. The stars you see in the sky at midnight tonight will not appear in the same configuration at midnight from the same place on the same date until somewhere around the year 28,000.

This, then, is the phenomenon of precession. What, however, is the explanation? Newton pointed out that the flattening of the Earth at the poles, combined with the fact that its orbit is inclined to the plane of the ecliptic by an angle of 23° 27',[16] means that the gravitational effect of the Sun and the Moon tends to tilt the equatorial plane towards the ecliptic.[17] This is what happens when a top spins: once the axis is tilted from the vertical, it will itself 'precess' round the vertical, if much more slowly than the top itself. Of the two forces – friction and gravitation – which make a top fall, friction plays no part in the interaction between the Sun,

54

the Earth and the Moon, while gravity, although the ultimate cause of the precession of the Earth, as described above, operates in such a way that the process continues indefinitely.

Because in every synodic month the new Moon is closest to the Sun and the full Moon farthest away, the effect of the Sun's gravity is slightly larger at the time of the new Moon. This is sufficient to cause a small cyclical variation in the Moon's orbit, which is observable as an 'inclination perturbation'. The effect is greatest when the Moon is at one or other of its nodes, since at these times it is either closest to the Sun or farthest away. The two extreme points of maximum and minimum perturbation are thus separated by half an eclipse year (173.3 days) so that a complete cycle lasts exactly one eclipse year. 'Inclination perturbation', although extremely small, is still a measurable quantity, and the fact that its cycle corresponds to that of the nodes makes it an accurate means of predicting eclipses.

The Saros

No book about solar eclipses is complete without a description of the *Saros*. This is the interval of just over 18 years, after which the sequence of eclipses repeats itself; the ancient Greeks knew of it, at least as an unexplained phenomenon. The Saros depends upon a coincidence in the dynamics of the Sun, the Moon and the Earth. Using the numbers already given on pages 46 and 47, it can be calculated that 223 synodic months (the length of the Saros) are equal to 6585.32 mean solar days, whereas 19 eclipse years are equal to 6585.78 mean solar days. The difference between the two periods (0.46 solar days) is just over 11 hours – not a very long time in the total Saros period of 18 years and 11 days. If this difference were zero, 223 synodic months would exactly

equal 19 eclipse years. Then, since the time between successive new Moons defines the synodic month, and the time
between successive alignments of the line of nodes NN' with
the Sun and Earth defines an eclipse year, any one eclipse
would repeat itself indefinitely at intervals equal to the Saros
period.

Taking, then, the Saros period to be 6585.32 mean solar
days, the odd fraction (0.32) of a day – a little short of 8
hours – would mean that the longitude of successive eclipses
would change by the angle through which the Earth rotates
in that time. The result is that the path of every third eclipse
in the series is about 10° west of that occurring 54 (3 × 18)
years earlier. This remains true despite the fact that the
period of 19 eclipse years is about 11 hours longer than 223
synodic months.

It is as a result of this small, 11-hour discrepancy that a
Saros series does not continue indefinitely, but has both a
beginning and an end. This is reflected in a long-term change
in latitude as the series progresses. For half the 42 series
running at any one time, the mean latitude of the eclipses
in the series progressively shifts from the north pole, past
the equator and on to the south pole; that is, the eclipses
move from above to below the ecliptic. In this half of the
series, the eclipsed Sun lies within the ecliptic limits of the
ascending node, N. The reverse process governs the eclipses
in the other half of the Saros series, which correspond to
the descending node, N'. By convention, the former case
defines Saros series with an odd number, while the latter
defines those with an even number.

In both cases, the first event in a series is a partial eclipse
close to a pole, with successive eclipses, at intervals of just
over 18 years, moving steadily in the direction of the other
pole, where the final event is, once again, a partial eclipse.
Totality occurs only in the middle of the series. The question
is, how many eclipses, whether partial or total, make up one

series? Now, the first eclipse in any Saros series occurs when the Sun and the Moon make contact just inside one of the ecliptic limits, as shown in Figure 2.4. Successive eclipses will occur ever closer to the node, until a point is reached when an eclipse occurs on the other side of it. The process then goes into reverse and continues until the final eclipse, when once again the Sun and Moon make contact just inside the other ecliptic limit. At the beginning and end of the series, the eclipses are partial, with a low magnitude: as noted on page 46, annular or total eclipses, as the case may be, occur only in the middle of the series.

The Sun takes a year of 365.2425 days to complete its 360° circuit of the ecliptic, so every day it moves 0.986° (or 59.14') eastwards.[18] The critical difference of 11 hours by which the period of 223 synodic months falls short of 19 eclipse years means that with every eclipse in a Saros series the sun falls 27' short of its position at the eclipse immediately preceding.[19] We know that the minimum distance between the ecliptic limits is 30.7°, and the maximum distance 37.02°. On this basis the mean distance of 33.86° is sufficient for 75 eclipses. This is a rough and ready calculation, and the actual number for the average Saros series is 73. This factor multiplied by the Saros period of 18 years and 11 days gives 1316 years as the length of an average Saros series.

On average there are 238 solar eclipses in a century, and a Saros period lasts 18.03 years. At any one time, 42 (238 × 18.03 years/100 years) Saros series must therefore be running, for there is never more than one eclipse belonging to the series in any one Saros period. Those who know the music of J. S. Bach might like to imagine a fugue in 42 parts, with a new part coming in, and an old one dropping out, at regular intervals in such a way that the actual number of parts remains constant throughout time.

Every Saros series has its own character, as a result of a

further arithmetical coincidence. As already shown above, the distance of the Moon from the Earth at the time of a solar eclipse is a key factor in defining its magnitude. The time taken by the Moon to return to its perigee defines what is called the anomalistic month, of 27.555 days; 239 such months are equal to 6585.54 days, which is just less than 19 eclipse years and just more than 223 synodic months – the two definitive periods for the Saros series. The very small margin means that successive eclipses in a Saros series occur at almost exactly the same point in an anomalistic month. This means, above all, that in the middle of such a series there is relatively little variation in the magnitude of successive eclipses.

If, for example, the Moon is close to perigee in successive eclipses, then the eclipses in the middle of the series will have a relatively high magnitude. This was the case with the Saros series which produced the longest eclipses of the twentieth century – at the requisite 18-year intervals – in 1901, 1919, 1937, 1955, 1973 and 1991. The longest duration was 7 minutes, 7 seconds on 20 June 1955: this was the 34th eclipse in a series of 70 which began in 1360 and will end in 2604. All the eclipses in this series will prove to have been total from that of 1703 until that of 2496: this is evidence of a very 'strong' Saros.

In 1887 the German astronomer Theodor von Oppolzer's monumental *Canon of Eclipses* was published posthumously. It listed all solar eclipses from the year 1207 BC, and numbered not only the Saros series but also the successive eclipses within each series. On this basis the eclipse of 11 August 1999 is number 21 out of the 77 which belong to Saros series 145, which will end in the year 3009.

The Saros series are a paradox in the history of eclipse astronomy. The name was adapted into English by Edmond Halley at the beginning of the eighteenth century; it is based on a phrase misunderstood by the Roman historian, Pliny

(23–79), who, in his 37-volume *Historia naturalis*, attributed the discovery of the phenomenon to the Babylonians. Although this attribution has hardly ever been disputed, the Babylonian astronomers must have been phenomenally good at keeping and interpreting records. The fact that only one out of every three successive solar eclipses in a Saros series could be observed within the bounds of the world as they knew it did not give them much to go by. None the less, in the recorded history of eclipses, the Saros series seem to have been at centre stage from the very beginning.

3

The Prehistoric Conundrum

Everything we know for certain about the accurate prediction of eclipses, in any part of the world, is linked to the
availability of written records. However, solar eclipses have
been happening, inexorably, in every part of the world, and
representatives of our species, *Homo sapiens sapiens*, have
been observing them as something out of the ordinary from
the very first moment that their intelligence was up to the
task of making this distinction. This was tens of thousands
of years before anyone had any idea of writing.

The question is, what, if anything, did the prehistoric
population make of the phenomenon of the solar eclipse?
The trouble is that the event itself is visible so seldom from
a given locality that very few of those alive at any one time
would have had any experience of it. What would such
people have made of an event which, as far as they were
concerned, nobody had ever witnessed, nor would anybody
be likely to do so at any future time? What is more, the
event itself, for those few who have experienced it, is over
in a matter of an hour or two, and however dramatic it may
be at the moment of climax it leaves no record of ever having

occurred. None the less, in the twentieth century, popular science has taught millions of people to believe that coming to terms with solar eclipses, in a way that required massive investment in time and energy, was a veritable obsession for some prehistoric populations – particularly those who made their homes on our own doorstep. The question is, is this a likely scenario for any prehistoric culture?

At the dawn of civilisation, observing the heavens and interpreting the observations, were ideally suited for being in the vanguard of science. Both day and night provided opportunities, at different seasons of the year, for recording significant astronomical events, and the transition between them, at sunrise and sunset, was particularly opportune. Some events, such as the first appearance of a given star at sunrise or its last appearance at sunset, could be observed without the help of any fixed points in the landscape. Such was the heliacal rising[1] of Sirius, the Dog Star, in ancient Egypt, which occurred at midsummer and heralded the annual Nile flood, essential for agriculture. Other records, as provided by the written language of Egypt, are necessary to inform us of the significance that was attached to such an event.

When we come to consider prehistory, the absence of written records makes the idea of an exact science much more problematical. Any branch of science both records and predicts the phenomena that define it (so that astronomy, for instance, is defined by its focus on celestial phenomena); the records, in whatever form they take, provide the basis of prediction. At an elementary level, the memory of a single individual is a sufficient record. Children who look at the night sky need no instruction (although they may well receive it) to learn that the phases of the Moon will repeat themselves at regular intervals. At a more advanced level, characteristic of *Homo sapiens sapiens*, the range of science can be greatly extended by the collective memory of a particular population. (This now sometimes goes under the name of 'folk memory' or 'oral tradition'.) Solar eclipses may become part of the tradition, even though no single instance is within the memory of any of those who have inherited the tradition. In relation to the hard sciences, traditional knowledge of this kind sometimes goes under the name of 'ethnoscience'.

A cumulative process develops as the predictions, whether or not they are fulfilled, become part of the record. In the course of time the observed phenomena begin to form a pattern and become structured in the minds of the observers. The Frenchman, Claude Lévi-Strauss, is well-known among anthropologists for his study and, above all, his documentation of this process. Once the structure is established, it will tend to incorporate any newly observed phenomena that fit into it. This happens even in a literate culture, for generally accepted patterns of thought are tenacious in holding their ground. But the history of science is punctuated by breakthroughs which undermine existing structures and lead to their eventual collapse. Just consider the success of Galileo's astronomy in the seventeenth century, even though the Church did everything possible to suppress it.

The lesson taught by Lévi-Strauss is that a structure will be imposed upon observed phenomena in such a way that relates them to other basic, and essentially unrelated, structures in the folk tradition. This may sound all very abstract, but folk astronomy illustrates the process in any number of ways – some of which may relate to eclipses.

The most elementary example is the recognition and naming of stars and constellations. The sky at night is essentially chaotic. Observed at a glance, it is no more than a random scattering of points of light of varying intensity, but a little imagination helped by elements retained in the folk memory will bring order out of chaos. (Even today, astronomers list stars by their order of brightness in constellations half of which were established two thousand and more years ago.) Once such a measure of organisation is achieved, it is then no great problem to incorporate into the tradition such events as the heliacal rising of Sirius. For all we know, this was regarded as significant long before the invention of writing enabled the people of Egypt to make a permanent record of it. This scenario seems quite probable, given first the importance of the annual Nile flood to Egyptian agriculture, and second the archaeological record of agriculture along the banks of the Nile at a time before there was any written language. At the end of the day, however, we simply do not know what the people inhabiting the Nile valley thought about Sirius in prehistoric times.

Abundant evidence from the written records of the earliest civilisations makes clear that configurations of the Sun and the Moon, the planets and the stars, involving various alignments and conjunctions, were noted and regarded as significant for one reason or another. In some cases (such as Sirius and the Nile floods) the phenomenon must come down to Earth, and be related somehow to the natural world.

This explains how a heavenly body can become significant when it is in line with fixed objects in the terrestrial landscape. These could be natural features: for instance, the exact day of the summer or winter solstice might be known from the fact that on that day the Sun set behind a line defined by a rock close by and a distant hill. But again, with no independent record that such observations were made, they would be completely lost to the history of astronomy.

The case becomes more interesting where observations are linked to objects carefully crafted by some human agency and placed deliberately at some specially chosen location. Megaliths, or 'giant stones', are found in many locations in north-west Europe, including the British Isles. These are particularly fascinating since they can be traced back to a time in prehistory for which there are few other records of the people who built them.[2] These vast monuments, useless for any practical purpose in any local economy, must none the less have been immensely important given the vast amount of labour required to erect them. Comparing them with later monuments, such as the pyramids of Egypt and Mexico, leads readily to the conclusion that they served some supernatural purpose, and written records from the earliest civilisations suggest that this was in some way connected to astronomical observation.

The argument becomes even more persuasive where there is not one megalith, but a whole configuration, such as is to be found at Carnac in north-west France or, in particular, Stonehenge in southern England (which may belong to a related culture). Nowhere in the world is there a site so old[3] which has been submitted to so much study and speculation, but whose actual use remains problematical. Without doubt there was much method and planning behind the construction of Stonehenge, which took place in at least three phases over a period lasting several centuries.

With so many stones it is not difficult to discover an axis, defined by two prominent megaliths, pointing in one direction to sunrise at the summer solstice, and in the other to sunset at the winter solstice. None the less, the process requires reading into the configuration of the stones a system of organisation for which there is no other evidence. The only argument, which is largely intuitive, is that the monument must have had *some* purpose, that that purpose was astronomical, and that any other purpose seems even more far-fetched. Even if we accept this argument, Stonehenge, or any other comparable configuration of megaliths, was still not necessarily used as an instrument of scientific astronomy in any modern sense. There are good reasons for believing that it was not, and that its main use was to establish the time of some important event in the ritual life of the local

population. This is the generally accepted view among pre-
historians, who have been able to make any number of fanciful suggestions (many now proved false) about what form
the rites took and what their purpose was. Again, in the
absence of any other records the answer to such questions
remains entirely speculative.

The question still remains as to why alignments of megaliths, however elaborate, cannot be regarded as some proto-
scientific instrument designed to discover the secret of
eclipses. Take a proto-civilisation, such as existed in Britain
some four thousand years ago, that builds monuments, such
as Stonehenge, which have some astronomical blueprint (of
which there will be no surviving record except the monuments themselves). Such a blueprint could have been significant only if it were based on observed phenomena: with
a monument such as Stonehenge, which clearly took many
years to build, these phenomena could not have been too
commonplace, for the work involved would then have been
quite out of proportion to the monument's usefulness. No
one has argued that Stonehenge was some sort of alarm
clock; on the other hand, if the astronomical phenomena
that provided the rationale for the whole operation took place
too seldom and irregularly, then the usefulness of perpetuat-
ing them, whether in heavy blocks of stone or as holes in
the ground, would have been much too problematic to justify
the exercise. With something as evanescent as a solar eclipse,
where partiality lasts little more than two hours, and totality
never more than eight minutes, could the dramatic impact
– as recalled by all those who have experienced totality –
ever have been that compelling?

Let us go back in our imaginations to a day, some four
to five thousand years ago, when a total solar eclipse was
witnessed by the population around Stonehenge. In a period
of a thousand years there will almost certainly have been
one such day (although the present canons of eclipses do

not go back that far). We can accept that the eclipse on that day caused consternation – a conclusion fully justified by existing documentation, from more recent historical periods, of popular reactions to solar eclipses. What is much more problematic for us is whether the event could be related to an earlier eclipse, occurring either in the lifetime of the oldest observers present or, more likely, in the local folklore transmitted from one generation to another.

Such a relationship, coupled with memories or tales of cataclysmic events attributed to the earlier eclipse, and the recognition of others occurring in conjunction with the present one, could have led to an imperative to establish some permanent means of dealing with such events if and when they should ever recur. Such an imperative does not necessarily need to be driven by a previous eclipse, but this would certainly add greatly to its force. At all events, aligning two markers pointing in the direction of totality as it was observed on the fateful day could be the starting point for any countermeasure, even though setting up the whole operation within the hour or two of partiality between first and second contact would not have been all that simple.

Everyday building materials such as wooden poles could no doubt have been used for some temporary structure, to be replaced in due time by a permanent stone structure waiting to be discovered and explained by archaeologists and astronomers some four thousand years later. This was hardly a scenario that the prehistoric workmen, or even those in authority over them, could have conceived of as they were getting on with the job. Suppose, however, that they completed it, so that the function of the stones as pointers to an eclipse became part of the local culture.

The ancient scenario then becomes even more problematical. So long as no further total eclipse occurs (and this can mean a period of hundreds of years) the eclipse monument can never be more than a local curiosity, equivalent

66

say to a hole dug by a thunderbolt (like the one that struck a garden at Marlborough, not far from Stonehenge, in 1989). It gains significance only with the occurrence of another total eclipse, which *could*, after all, occur within a period of a few years (as happened in the same part of England at the beginning of the eighteenth century). In this event, the second eclipse – inevitably, in a quite different part of the sky and at a different time of day – is certain to confound the monument to the first.

Not only will the established tradition, and the rites associated with it, require revision, but the monument will have to take this into account, so another stone or two are added. Given the uncertain and infrequent appearance of the basic phenomenon, the cumulative process will be extremely haphazard to say the least. The possibility of it being continued over hundreds of years, so at the end there emerges a definitive configuration of stones which can be used as a reliable recorder and predictor of eclipses, is far-fetched – and that is putting it mildly. This is a long way from anything that Lévi-Strauss would recognise as a structure (in the cognitive sense). It is not surprising, then, that no serious scholar, whether archaeologist or astronomer, has ever suggested that this is the way things actually happened.

At first sight the above argument is not quite fair to those who contend that Stonehenge was designed and built, with the prediction of eclipses as one, if not its main, intended use. The whole layout is far too complex to have been built for just this purpose. On the other hand, the alleged use of Stonehenge for predicting eclipses is based upon arguments which are both far-fetched and mutually incompatible. Some depend upon selected alignments of the megaliths, others on the so-called Aubrey holes. I have chosen to focus on the latter, but my reasons for refuting it apply equally to the former.

The outermost circle of Stonehenge consists of 56 holes, filled with local chalk rubble, discovered by the antiquarian John Aubrey in the seventeenth century, and now named after him. Carbon dating and other modern scientific procedures have established that the Aubrey stones belong to the earliest of three stages of construction extending over a period which may have been as long as a thousand years. It follows that if the great stone circles of the later stages related to phenomena of the Sun and Moon, such as their rising and setting at midsummer and midwinter – events which are more regular and frequent than eclipses – then it must be accepted that the builders of the first stage, whoever they were, started with the most difficult problem – predicting eclipses – and with no help at all from the sort of information the later stages might have provided them with.

What, then, is the basis of the argument that the purpose of the Aubrey holes was to predict eclipses? The answer is to be found in one of those coincidences which constantly occur in the science of eclipses.[4] There are 56 Aubrey holes, and 56 divided by 3, is 18.67, while 18.61 measures the number of years in the rotation of the line of nodes of the lunar orbit. This is too good to be true, unless, of course, the number 56 was chosen with this coincidence in mind. But then, by what process had the builders of Stonehenge discovered the 18.61-year period of the regression of the nodes of the lunar orbit?

I do not really need to answer this question, since I do not accept that any stage at Stonehenge was designed to predict eclipses. Instead, the counter-argument (which I find conclusive) is given clearly by John North:

All interpretations of Stonehenge as an eclipse computer are based on the idea that the counters (whether Aubrey holes or stones) were for keeping track of cycles of eclipses that had somehow been previously appreciated. [None of them] . . . have any serious regard for what was known of the history of the computational techniques that would have been required. There is no historical evidence whatsoever for this approach to eclipse calculation. From a single location only about half of all eclipses could have been observed, and no explanation was offered of how any simple theory of eclipses could ever have been developed in the first place.[5]

In truth, the use of the Aubrey holes as an eclipse predictor implies a virtual universe called into being some four thousand years before the computer age. The right configuration (which occurs once in every 18.61-year cycle of the nodes) of holes is then a necessary, but far from sufficient condition, for an eclipse to occur.

You have to get the picture right: on the basis of the existing knowledge of eclipses (acquired *a fortiori* without the help of the Aubrey holes) and a reasonable grasp of the mathematical theory of congruences (which deals with the sort of coincidences required by the whole procedure), a population in the middle of what is now Wiltshire marks out a large circle, and at equal intervals around it digs 56 holes and fills them with rubble. People then wait for an eclipse to occur, and once it does, on E-day, they start moving the markers, in the pre-ordained manner, around the Aubrey holes. Some have to be moved every six or seven days, others less frequently. At regular intervals corrections for the Sun and Moon markers are required. What happens at the end of the cycle, more than eighteen years later? The answer is nothing that can be observed after all that time and trouble. At best a necessary condition has been satisfied for an eclipse that in practice will not occur, or at least not so that it can be seen by observers anywhere near Wiltshire. (On this point I must take issue with John North, if he really means to suggest that 'half of all eclipses can be observed from a single location': even allowing for the observation of partial eclipses, the proportion observable from a single location is much smaller.)

It is all a bit discouraging. An eclipse happens, but any attempt to find some rhyme or reason for it in terms of existing astronomical knowledge is doomed to failure. It is a one-off event which fits only one of the known regularities of the heavens – the occurrence of a new Moon. The beginning of a new synodic month is not much to go by, but as a clue it is better than nothing. But just how many synodic months must pass before the phenomenon can again be seen by observers in the same locality remains a mystery: the average number of synodic months between total eclipses, 4,638, is simply daunting, and the people who built Stonehenge had no way of even finding a close approximation to this figure. The interval between partial eclipses would have been much shorter, but even so, in a culture without any form of record-keeping – except for the monoliths – the use of such intervals for building any useful base for computation is extremely problematical, to say the least.

When it comes to the prediction of eclipses, no other known prehistoric site has a better claim than Stonehenge. If the case for Stonehenge fails, then it must fail everywhere. The argument extends to any artefact, such as the Ishango Bone, which was found in Central Africa and is older than any known megalithic site. This bone is marked with three columns of notches, but there is, needless to say, no independent record of their significance. It has been suggested that they record phases of the Moon,[6] but this is pure speculation. The conclusion is simple: although, very occasionally, our distant ancestors must have observed solar eclipses in the course of some hundred thousand years of prehistory, they always lacked the basic mathematical resources to develop any sort of theory about their occurrence. The question is, how much wiser did humans become when they entered into the realm of recorded history?

Whatever the Ishango Bone may have meant, it was a forerunner in a process in which whole numbers, or integers, came to be systematically represented in the permanent form of numerals. The case of the *quipus*, knotted strings used by the Incas in pre-colonial America to record numerals, demonstrates that such means can exist independently of any system of recording spoken language in permanent form. The Incas, in contrast to the Mayas of Central America, never achieved this. So be it: nothing suggests that *quipus* were ever used for recording numbers for astronomical purposes. The Incas, like any long-established population, must from time to time have witnessed eclipses of both the Sun and the Moon. No doubt they sought to explain and interpret them, but what they thought, and how they reacted, are to us today a closed book. The same must be true about those who built Stonehenge, and every other prehistoric population to which our ancestors belonged. Without the faculty of writing, these remote ancestors of ours got nowhere when it came to developing a systematic astronomy of eclipses.

What is really puzzling today, at the end of the second millennium, is how readily theories about the use of Stonehenge for predicting eclipses are accepted and incorporated into books and articles covering this subject. Bryan Brewer's *Eclipse*, published in a new edition for the eclipse visible from Hawaii on 11 July 1991, devotes two whole pages[7] to Stonehenge, in a book with less than a hundred pages of text. Now the record had been set straight by John North's *Stonehenge: Neolithic Man and the Cosmos*, which presents an unanswerable case against the use of Stonehenge as an eclipse predictor.

Whatever the shortcomings of prehistoric astronomy – in any part of the world – the position was changed entirely once it became possible to keep permanent records of celestial phenomena. This required the invention of writing. The consequences of this invention for astronomy provide the theme for the next chapter.

4

The Premodern History of Eclipses

Science and civilisation

Astronomy, like any natural science, can be taken to have its essential basis in hard facts, capable of being discovered either by observation or experiment. The facts are always there, but the process of discovery is a human activity, and as such is part of history. Corresponding to the facts that are known at any one time is an understanding and explanation of them which depend upon both their historical context and the workings of the human mind. Within any recognised population, with its own characteristic language, religion, political and economic systems, the history of science begins when that population divides into two classes. One, large and general, approaches facts intuitively, and interprets them in a way that accords with the experiences of everyday life. The other class, small and specialised, is systematic in its approach, and is concerned above all that any interpretation of the facts should be consistent and free from contradictions. In a rough and ready way (which is convenient for the present chapter) the world-view of the first class may be called 'popular', and of the second 'scientific'. Once this division occurs in a population, it is on the way to becoming 'civilised', and both its new state, and the process by which it emerges, define 'civilisation'.[1] How precisely the achievements of the scientists are applied in the interests of the population as a whole is a different question, with any number of possible answers (many of which will come up in later chapters). It is worth noting, however, that being 'civilised' in this sense does not confer an automatic right to claim the moral high ground. This may be how people thought a hundred years ago, but any serious history of civilisation (including the scientific community) casts serious doubts on any such claim.

The division between popular and scientific is not clearcut. For one thing, the body of empirical knowledge (defined by hard facts established by scientific observation and experiment) is extremely heterogeneous, as witness such diverse modern disciplines as genetics, physics, geology and, indeed, astronomy. This, inevitably, is reflected in the world of scientists, which is a world of specialists. Although specialists in different fields may find it difficult to understand one another's work, they still tend to have a common 'scientific' mind-set, coupled with an inclination to work professionally in their own communities, which have distinctive names such as 'universities', 'laboratories' and 'observatories'. Characteristic of such communities is the possession of cultural resources, such as writing, and special instruments for measurement and calculation, not found in the everyday domain. This means that the development of such resources is an important part of the history of any exact science, particularly in its early days.

One lesson from history is that science is only too often denied the freedom to develop in accordance with its own ideals. Science in practice tends to be applied science, and its practitioners are well advised to recognise the cultural

74

realpolitik of their own civilisation. This factor can never be disregarded when it comes to looking at how ancient populations dealt with eclipses (and the same is true of some of our contemporaries). Advancement of knowledge was never an end in itself: the process was encouraged when the knowledge to be gained could be applied to serve ends which were essentially unscientific. This was always particularly true of eclipses, since, in the true course of nature, there was never – and there never will be – any practical benefits to come from increased knowledge and understanding of the phenomenon. The benefits, more often imaginary than real, were to be found outside the realms of science as we know it.

Babylon

The earliest recorded numbers in the Old World are to be found on *bullae*, clay envelopes for carrying tokens used for accounting purposes in ancient Mesopotamia. At some stage, after the *bullae* had been used for some thousands of years, it was realised that a clay tablet, inscribed with the same symbols that appeared on the tokens, but without any actual contents, would serve the purpose just as well. Virtual tokens replaced the real thing. In contrast to the Inca empire with its *quipus*, in Mesopotamia this transition led to the emergence of a written language:

> the appearance of writing . . . represents a logical step in the evolution of a system of record-keeping that originated some 11,000 years ago . . . Images of the tokens . . . supplanted the tokens themselves, and the evolution of symbolic objects led to the . . . adoption of writing all across western Asia.[2]

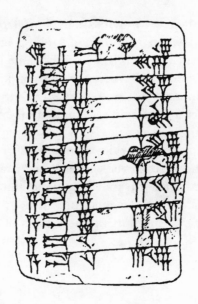

Figure 4.1 A Babylonian clay tablet, showing arithmetic in cuneiform script.

The transition to a complete writing system took a long time.
Sumerian writing, using pictographs as phonetic symbols for
recording speech, emerged in Uruk in about 3000 BC. This
was the beginning of a process which about a thousand years
later led to the emergence of cuneiform, a phonetical system
of writing engraved on clay tablets, which came to be used
throughout the Middle East. From the beginning numerals
were part of the system, and from about 2000 BC arithmetical
texts, such as that illustrated in Figure 4.1, begin to appear.
An exhaustive examination of these texts by the Oxford
scholar Eleanor Robson[3] (who is both a mathematician and
an Assyriologist) has failed to disclose any relating to astronomy until a very late period. It is significant that for a period
of a thousand years (roughly the second millennium BC) the
first population equipped with the cultural resources needed

for serious mathematics failed to apply them in this way. However, they did establish a system of counting, based on 60, which survives to this day in the measurement of both time and angles – an essential resource for any useful progress in astronomy. The period ended with the emergence of the great empire of Assyria, with its capital at Nineveh. Within this empire interest in eclipses, as revealed by the archaeological record, first arose, at a very late stage, with the eclipse of 769 BC. In the world of eclipse astronomy, this is about all that Assyria is remembered for.

A new empire, that of Babylon, showed from its earliest days in the eighth century BC an interest in eclipses unparalleled in human history. Today the cuneiform records made by Babylonians of both the time and place of solar eclipses are an invaluable resource for modern science. (About 98 per cent of the two thousand odd extant tablets are now in the British Museum.) A short summary of the history of Babylon[4] will put these records in their proper context. Some hundreds of years after an earlier empire had been destroyed by the Hittites in the middle of the second millennium BC, a new empire arose in the ninth century. Its capital, the new city of Babylon, became famous for its massive walls and the hanging gardens, which were counted among the Seven Wonders of the Ancient World.

The first eclipse referred to in the surviving records was a lunar eclipse in the reign of King Nabonassar in the eighth century: his death, in 733 BC, was followed by a century of renewed Assyrian domination, but King Nabopolassar (625–605 BC) turned the tables on Assyria, eliminated its empire and in 612 BC destroyed its capital, Nineveh. His successor, Nebuchadnezzar (605–562 BC), brought Babylon to the height of its power and established an empire extending to the shores of the Mediterranean.

In 538 BC the Babylonian Empire fell to the Persian Emperor Cyrus, and after two centuries of Persian rule

Alexander the Great annexed it in 330 BC. Alexander intended to make the city of Babylon his eastern capital, but this was not to be, since he died there, aged only 33, in 323 BC. He was succeeded by one of his generals, Seleucus. In 275 BC King Antiochus I (281–261 BC), son and successor to Seleucus, moved the capital to a new site some 100 km to the north, which he named Seleucia in honour of his father. This was, effectively, the end of Babylon, a great empire, known in the history of astronomy for its obsession with eclipses. From the reign of Nabonassar in the eighth century to that of Antiochus in the third, Babylon had lasted, with varying fortunes, for nearly five hundred years. Even after this period, cuneiform astronomical texts continued to be written; the last surviving record of a total solar eclipse refers to that of 15 April 136 BC. This establishes an astonishing period of at least six hundred years for the Babylonian eclipse records. The recorded lunar eclipses continue for another seventy odd years, ending at 67 BC.[5]

The lesson is clear: if you want to know about eclipses, you must look first at Babylon. But what forms do the records take? Three are important when it comes to eclipses. First are the diaries, texts containing day-to-day information over periods of six or seven months. These record historical events, such as the death and accession of kings, economic factors such as commodity prices, geographical and meteorological data such as the level of the River Euphrates, and, above all, astronomical data including the occurrences of eclipses. The problem with the diaries is that few survive from the period before the fourth century, whereas they cover the majority of years from 385 BC down to 60 BC.

The second form taken by the records is tables listing the occurrence of particular phenomena, such as eclipses. These have the advantage of being based on occurrences for which no diary records have ever been found, but they are of much more use for lunar than for solar eclipses. They can, however, cover very long periods of time: one table, covering 912 eclipse possibilities (both observations and predictions) over a period lasting from the eighth to the fourth century BC, and relating to 24 Saros cycles, is our best evidence for the discovery of the Saros in the very earliest days of Babylonian astronomy.

So-called 'goal-year' texts are the third form of records. These relate recorded astronomical events (including eclipses) to a selected future goal year, so they are important in establishing the importance of such events as portents for what will happen in the goal year. Their usefulness, to date, is limited by the fact that very few translations have so far been published. Accurate dating, however, is no great problem.

In all the records so far found there is, however, no table of solar eclipses, and none before that of 370 BC is mentioned in any of the records. None the less, the recorded Babylonian observations of solar eclipses are unequalled as a resource for exploring the ancient history of eclipse observation. The main reason is the accuracy with which these records pinpoint the time and place of eclipses. On this point the Babylonian records leave those from other parts of the ancient world far behind. What is more, a Babylonian prediction of a solar eclipse almost never failed to come true, although its actual occurrence could be in a part of the world remote from Babylon.

The question remains as to just how well the Babylonians actually understood the cause of eclipses. However, before answering this question it is worth noting how well favoured they were for practising serious observational astronomy. To begin with, the city of Babylon (from which all important observations were made) could hardly have been better placed geographically. Located on a vast flat plane, whose distant horizons were invaluable for measuring the altitudes of heavenly bodies, it had the additional advantage of an exceptionally dry desert climate ensuring an abundance of clear skies with few clouds to hide these bodies from observers. At the same time, Babylonian civilisation became increasingly sophisticated in its measurement of time. Last but not least, its cuneiform writing made possible not only the recording of astronomical information for posterity, but also communication with the farthest reaches of an extensive empire.

So, did the Babylonians make any sort of astronomical breakthrough? On this point, none of the surviving clay tablets contains anything which could be called a scientific text. The rules used to predict eclipses required no deep theory, simply an extrapolation from past records. In spite of the extraordinarily quality, to say nothing of the volume, of these records, Babylon may well have acquired any actual understanding it had of the cause of eclipses from the Greeks during the period of the Seleucid kings, following the reign of Alexander the Great. During this Hellenistic period, the interaction between the Babylonian astronomers with their meticulous compilation of accurate records, and the Greeks with their unparalleled gift for theory, could have lifted astronomy to new heights. The question (to be answered in the following section) is just how far this theory went when it came to eclipses.

Two factors explain why the astronomical achievements of the ancient world were preserved for posterity in a way that frustrated further development. First, after the time of Ptolemy (about AD 100–170) the achievements of the previous centuries were transmitted in the canonical form he had given them in the *Almagest*, his monumental encyclopedia of astronomy. The underlying principle that the Earth was at the centre of the Solar System set Western astronomy on the wrong course for more than a thousand years. Second, the Greeks and the Hebrews, by adopting a written notation for numbers based on the letters of the alphabet, made useful calculations next to impossible for a similar length of time. Roman numerals were no better. In the ancient world the Babylonian number system, which had 60 instead of 10 as its base, was much superior.[6] After the time of Ptolemy its main legacy proved to be the subdivisions of 60 in the units used in measuring angles and time, largely as a result of the Arabs preserving and continuing to use the *Almagest*.

At the end of the day, Babylonian astronomers were never in business as pure scientists. They were almost certainly priests of some kind, and as such they were, at best, applied scientists, and for the applications required by the people of Babylon and their rulers, their actual results were more than sufficient. Except for the fact that Babylon, at some time in the course of its history, recognised the Saros series, the constant preoccupation with eclipses and other celestial phenomena contributed practically nothing to the advance of astronomy as a science. Quite simply, those who observed and recorded these phenomena with such precision were not scientists in any sense that we would recognise today.

Greece

In the sixth year of the war, which [the Medes and Lydians] had carried on with equal fortunes, an engagement took place in which it turned out that when the battle was in progress the day suddenly became night. This alteration of the day Thales the Miletian foretold to the Ionians, setting as its limit this year in which the change actually occurred. When the Lydians and the Medes saw the day turned to night, they ceased from fighting, and both were the more zealous to make peace. (Herodotus)

Some think he was the first to study the heavenly bodies and to foretell eclipses of the Sun ... for which reason both Xenophanes and Herodotus express admiration; and both Heraclitus and Democritus bear witness for him. (Diogenes Laertius)

Eudemus relates in the history of Astronomy that ... Thales [first discovered] the eclipse of the sun and the variable period of its solstices. (Decyllides)

These three passages from the Greek classics[7] refer to the best-known scientist, Thales, of the pre-Socratic era, and to an event, the battle between the Medes and Lydians, whose outcome he was involved in as a result of predicting the solar eclipse described by Herodotus. There is nothing equivalent to them from the rest of the ancient world.

Thales, like many of his Greek successors, and unlike anyone known from the Babylonian records, was recognisably a scientist in the modern sense. In the words of a noted Cambridge mathematician, J. E. Littlewood (1885–1977), he could have been a 'fellow of another college'. He was someone who, in a conversation with Littlewood, would have been on the same wavelength, whereas with the Babylonians who produced the myriad clay tablets Littlewood would have got nowhere. Even so, from our knowledge both of Greek astronomy at the time of Thales, and of Thales' own work in other fields of mathematics, we can be certain that he neither knew of, nor established, a 'scientific theory of the true cause of eclipses.'[8]

If Thales, as Herodotus records, did predict a solar eclipse, he could only have done so on the basis of a long series of recorded observations now completely lost. Conceivably he knew of the Babylonian records, but the surviving tablets do not record any *series* of solar eclipses from before the time of Thales. (There is, however, an eclipse recorded in a poem by the seventh-century Greek Archilochus: modern eclipse theory assigns it to either 657 or 648 BC. This may be useful for dating the poem, but one eclipse could hardly have helped Thales, whatever records he may have had of it.)

The ancient world appears to have had few doubts about Thales' ability to predict eclipses. According to Pliny, writing in the first century,

> the original discovery (of the cause of eclipses) was made in Greece by Thales of Miletus, who in the fourth year of the 48th Olympiad [585/4 BC] foretold the eclipse of the Sun that occurred in the reign of Alyattes, in the 170th year after the foundation of Rome [584/3 BC].[9]

Pliny records what would certainly have been an important event in the history of astronomy, if it had actually occurred. This is a very big 'if'. The recorded material known to us from before the time of Thales contains neither the empirical records required for Thales' discovery, nor any astronomical theory from which it could have been developed.

The present state of the game is stated by Otto Neugebauer (who was the leading twentieth-century scholar of the ancient history of science) in his *History of Ancient Mathematical Astronomy*:

> In the early days of classical studies one did not assume that in the sixth century BC a Greek philosopher had at his disposal the astronomical and mathematical tools necessary to predict a solar eclipse. But then one could invoke the astronomy of the 'Chaldeans' from whom Thales could have received whatever information was required. This hazy but convenient theory collapsed in view of the present knowledge of Babylonian astronomy ... It is now evident that even three centuries after Thales no solar eclipse could be predicted to be visible in Asia

Minor – in fact not even for Babylon. There remains another vague hypothesis: the prediction by means of cycles (if need be again available on request from Babylon). But unfortunately there exists no manageable cycle of solar eclipses visible at a given locality . . .[10]

F. R. Stephenson hammers the final nail into the coffin:

In brief, the assertions of Herodotus and Pliny probably owe their origin to the various legends which accumulated around the personality of Thales.[11]

Did anyone do any better than Thales in later centuries? After all, these 'fellows of another college' included Plato, Aristotle, Archimedes and, last but not least, Ptolemy. It was none of these, but their forerunner, Anaxagoras of Clazomenae (500–428 BC), who became the first astronomer to explain eclipses of both the Sun and Moon correctly. All we know of this achievement is recorded by Hippolytus:

The Moon has not any light of its own but derives it from the Sun . . . Eclipses of the Moon are due to its being screened by the Earth, or sometimes by the bodies beneath the Moon; those of the Sun to screening by the Moon when it is new . . . the Moon was made of Earth, and had plains and ravines on it.[12]

Anaxagoras himself wrote only one, probably very short book, which is known today only from a few fragments recorded by other authors. Since he dealt with a multitude of topics (most quite unrelated to astronomy), it is doubtful whether his treatment of eclipses went any further than Hippolytus' record. In any case, Anaxagoras was a thinker rather than an observer, a theorist rather than an empiricist, so that his single statement of an important scientific truth must represent his entire legacy to the science of eclipses. As such, it may still be worth more than any other inheritance from the classical period, because unless you realise that eclipses are caused by the alignment of the Sun, the Earth and the Moon, in one order or another, you get nowhere in understanding or explaining them.

We move on from Anaxagoras, the philosopher, to Thucydides, the historian. The latter's history of the Peloponnesian War (431–404 BC) is significant for being the first European text to mention stars appearing during a solar eclipse. This is somewhat problematic, since the only possible eclipse is that of 3 August 431 BC, whose magnitude was too small. This means that no star or planet would have been visible, except possibly Venus, some 19° east of the eclipsed Sun.

The next significant astronomer to make use of eclipses was Hipparchus of Nicaea, in the second century BC. He is recorded as having estimated the distance of the Earth from the Sun on the basis of the observation of one and the same solar eclipse in two different places, the Hellespont (now in Turkey, and better known as the Dardanelles) and Alexandria (in Egypt). Hipparchus nowhere suggests that he himself witnessed the eclipse, which could have occurred at any time between the founding of Alexandria in 331 BC and his own death in about 120 BC. The most likely date for the eclipse is 20 November 129 BC, which would have been total at the Hellespont, and 80 per cent at Alexandria, as Hipparchus recorded. These measurements would also have provided the result of $67\frac{1}{3}$ Earth radii as the distance between the Earth and the Moon, as calculated by Hipparchus. Further confirmation comes from the fact that Hipparchus' result is remarkably close to the actual distance, now known to be 60.25 Earth radii.

It was also Hipparchus who, on the basis of eclipse records (including some from Babylon), established unprecedentedly accurate measurements of the Moon in its orbit, and the various periods occurring in its monthly cycle. Their basis, a period of 126,007 days plus one hour (almost exactly 345 years), gives some idea of the sophistication of his methods. It did not matter that his whole understanding of the movement of the Sun, the Moon and the five planets known in his day was based on the theory of epicycles, which effectively placed the Earth at the centre of the Solar System. Hipparchus was still able to predict eclipses, and other events such as the occultation of a planet by the Moon, with an accuracy that would stand the test of time for about seventeen centuries, until the era of modern astronomy was ushered in by Copernicus, Tycho Brahe, Kepler, Galileo and, ultimately, Newton.

In the first century AD the Greek philosopher Plutarch published a dialogue entitled *The Face of the Moon*, which contains a description of a solar eclipse in which 'many stars shine out from many parts of the sky and tempered the air in the manner of twilight'.[13] Elaborate calculations based on modern eclipse data identify Plutarch's eclipse as that observed from Chaeroneia, near Delphi, on 20 March AD 71. Since Plutarch had a passion for recording solar eclipses, many occurring long before his own day (if they occurred at all), his writing of history on this matter must always be taken with a grain of salt.

Finally we come to the eclipse observed from Alexandria on 16 June 364, which Theon of Alexandria recorded with a precision not to be found in any other account from the Greek or Hellenistic world:

> . . . the exact ecliptic conjunction . . . took place according to the Egyptian calendar in the 1112th year from the reign of Nabonassar . . . on the 24th of Thoth . . . time of the beginning of contact . . . $2\frac{5}{6}$ equinoctial hours after midday and the time of the middle of the eclipse . . . $3\frac{4}{5}$ hours, and the time of complete restoration . . . $4\frac{1}{2}$ hours after the said midday . . .[14]

The story of Greek astronomy really ends with Ptolemy, who lived in Alexandria in the second century AD. He is noted for the compilation of a vast encyclopedia of astronomy entitled, in the original Greek, *Megale syntaxis*, but known today by its Arabic title, *Almagest* (which means, simply, 'The Greatest'). For eclipses, Ptolemy simply incorporated the results of Hipparchus, at the same time adopting and elaborating his theory of epicycles. The result was to establish an astronomical paradigm in the Western world which, because of its basic premise that the Earth was fixed at the centre of the Universe, achieved canonical status in the Catholic Church.

In their approach to astronomy, Hipparchus, Ptolemy – indeed the whole school of Greek astronomy - were geometers rather than physicists. True, the orbits of the heavenly bodies as defined by the theory of epicycles were given a physical explanation, but this had no empirical basis and was derived entirely from the requirements of the geometry. What is so remarkable about the work of the Greek astronomers is that they were continually able to improve upon their geometrical model to take into account every new measurement of the phenomena it was supposed to explain. In the end it was the physics of the model, not its geometry, which proved to be its Achilles' heel, but this did not become apparent until the work of the Danish astronomer, Tycho Brahe, in the sixteenth century.

China

The records of the Chinese empire, written in the thousands of distinctive characters still to be found in today's standard forms, contain more references to solar eclipses that those of any other ancient civilisation. The earliest possible record of a solar eclipse refers to that seen from An-yang (36.07°N,

108.88°E) on 5 June 1302 BC. Because this was long before written Chinese became standard during the time of the Han dynasty (206 BC to AD 220), it contains a number of key characters whose meaning is now uncertain. Stephenson gives two versions:

(i) Diviner Ko: . . . day *i-mao* to dawn, fog. Three flames ate the Sun. Big stars.

(ii) On the next day *i-mao* it may not be sunny. The King read the cracks and said, 'There will be disaster but it will not rain'. On day *i-mao* it was foggy; when it came to the time of the . . . meal, the day greatly cleared.[15]

Originally, Chinese texts were inscribed on the bones of animals: the shoulder-blade of an ox and the lower shell of a turtle both provide a sufficiently large flat surface for writing on. Some 150,000 such bones have now been discovered in the area around An-yang, the capital city of the Shang dynasty which ruled in China from about 1500 to 1050 BC. They are known now as 'oracle bones', simply because of the nature of the texts inscribed upon them. The oracle itself was to be found in cracks appearing across the bone after it had been heated.[16] The king, or one of his astrologers, would interpret the cracks, and the interpretation would then be inscribed on the bone. This is the origin of the text (written on a turtle's shell) quoted above, which may be the earliest known written record of a solar eclipse from any part of the world.

Both versions of the text confirm its astrological importance. This was to remain the principle reason for recording eclipses (and any number of other astronomical events) right down to the beginning of the modern age of China in the twentieth century. Both versions also refer to the day *i-mao*, and this requires some explanation. At least from the time of the Shang dynasty, Chinese calendars have depended on a repeating cycle of 60 possible combinations (*kan-chih*) of the ten signs for the so-called 'heavenly stems' (*t'ien kan*) and the twelve 'earthly branches' (*ti-chih*). Every point in the cycle is defined by one sign from each category; *i-mao*, according to this rule, is number 52. The use of the *kan-chih* for establishing days in the calendar still continues at the level of popular astrology, and since the system has never once been interrupted in more than 3,000 years, every *i-mao* date is known for every single day for the whole of Chinese history.

The approximate date of the *i-mao* turtle shell is 1300 BC. It would be too good to be true if a modern canon of eclipses recorded a solar eclipse occurring on an *i-mao* day, some time around this year, with totality observable from An-yang. Totality, however, was to be seen on: 5 June 1302 BC – a *ping-ch'en* day, number 53 in the *kan-chih* series – just one day out. Does this matter?

On this question it would be easy to take an 'orientalist' view, and assume that a single day was neither here nor there in Shang China. This is too easy a way out. The court astrologers were obsessed with precision; they were also the emperor's closest advisers. If errors of one day occurred in other records it would be a different matter, but they do not. Every clear night the heavens were closely observed, particularly when a significant astronomical event, such as the conjunction of a planet with a star, was expected. An astrologer who had to tell the emperor, 'Come back tomorrow', would not have found favour. So where does this leave us? We just have to continue to study the records until we reach a point where the *kan-chih* problem does not arise.

Before doing so, one point is worth noting in the first translation, given above, of the *i-mao* text. The Sun is reported as being eaten by flames. To this day the Chinese for a solar eclipse if *rìshí*, literally 'Sun-eat', just as a lunar eclipse is *yuèshí*, or 'Moon-eat'. In both cases it is some heavenly monster that was supposed to be doing the eating. Since this traditional explanation of eclipses has survived in East and South-East Asia until the present day, there was never much of a chance for any scientific approach to explaining the physics of eclipses. No matter – the Chinese court astrologers, like the Babylonian priests (but unlike the Greeks), were not in business as scientists.

It is time to return to the records, and look for an eclipse recorded in China in a way that leaves no doubt about its actual occurrence. From the An-yang eclipse we have to move forward nearly six centuries, past the change from the Shang to the Chou dynasty in the eleventh century BC, to the total[17] eclipse of 17 July 709 BC, the first Chinese solar eclipse that can be dated unambiguously from the Chinese annals. This is also the first of some 36 solar eclipses recorded in the *Ch'un-Ch'iu*, or annals of spring (*ch'un*) and autumn (*ch'iu*), reputed to have been edited by Confucius and covering the period 722–481 BC. The continuous record of solar eclipses (together with other astronomical events) is the earliest from any part of the world. It appears that solar eclipses, which always occur at new Moon, were used to regulate the calendar – a practice continued in the world of modern science. Almost certainly, the observations were from a single place, Ch'u-fu, the capital city of the state of Lu where Confucius had his home.

The records of the eclipse ceremonies at Ch'u-fu always mention that drums were beaten and oxen sacrificed at the temple: the loud noise of the drums (and in later accounts, gongs also) was to frighten away the dragon seen to be eating the Sun, and the oxen were to give him something else to eat instead. On the other hand, a text referring to a plea (made in 597 BC) to save from execution a general defeated in battle suggests that the Chinese well knew that once an eclipse was over, the order of the cosmos was restored: 'His defeat is like an eclipse of the Sun or the Moon; does it harm the brightness [of these bodies]?'[18] Eclipses continued to be recorded after the end of the spring and autumn period. The record for 24 October 444 BC is the first in history, from any part of the world, that mentions stars appearing, although since the eclipse was annular this seems somewhat problematical.

Written Chinese in its present form came into its own in the Han period (206 BC to AD 220). This critical development in Chinese cultural history relates to the invention of paper in the first century BC, which made it possible for records to be published on an unprecedented scale. From this period on, the records of eclipses almost invariably agree with modern calculations. The first Han emperor, Kao Tzu, also built China's first observatory, at his capital Ch'ang-an, and from that time the empire was never without one. Uniquely in Chinese history before the Ming dynasty (1368–1644), the end of the Han period also records eclipses observed at provincial locations.

Throughout the Han period the work of the astronomers at the imperial observatory was secret, for any unusual event observed was interpreted either as warning the emperor (who since the fourth century BC had been regarded as the son of Heaven) of impending danger, or as criticising him for misrule. Of all such events, a solar eclipse was the most foreboding, the gravity of its consequences depending directly on how close it was to totality. Chinese court records of eclipses continued to be made in substantially the same form through many different dynasties, a period which ended with the conquest of China by the Mongols, who were to rule the whole country from 1276 to 1368. This was the achievement of the first emperor of the Yuan dynasty (1271–1368), known to history as Kublai Khan (whose grandfather, Genghis Khan, had ruled the Mongol empire from his capital at Samarkand).

The Ming dynasty broke the tradition. Its official history, the *Ming-shi*, records no solar eclipses, but from 1500 onwards provincial histories make up for the loss, and contain many records proved to be accurate by modern computations. By this time also, the Chinese had become reasonably accurate in the prediction of eclipses, but like the Greeks and Babylonians they relied entirely on numerical cycles. For the court astrologers accurate prediction was doubly important: first, it testified to their professional skills, and second, it enabled them to recommend the countermeasures to be taken when the eclipse finally occurred. The tendency was to over-predict, for it was easier to find an excuse for an eclipse that failed to occur (a non-event with no untoward consequences) than to explain their failure to predict an eclipse that did occur, and for which the necessary remedy had not been prepared in advance. It could well be that reported eclipses not confirmed by any of the modern canons are in fact no more than eclipses which were predicted but failed to occur. The difference between prediction and actual occurrence is not always apparent from the records.

The Ming dynasty witnessed the transformation of Chinese science as the result of the first contacts with European learning in the late sixteenth century. Notwithstanding Marco Polo's presence (1271–92) at the court of Kublai Khan, it was the arrival in 1582 of Jesuit missionaries, led by Matteo Ricci (1552–1610), that was to transform Chinese science. For ten years before going to China, Ricci had received special training in Rome in mathematics, astronomy and other branches of the natural sciences, followed by a year in Macao devoted to learning the Chinese language.

Ricci paid particular attention to Chinese court astrology, and impressed by his ability to predict eclipses more accurately than the Chinese. By demonstrating the instruments of European science, such as clocks and maps of the world, and adapting their use to Chinese traditional science, Ricci won many converts to the Church. The Jesuit mission continued after his death. It brought the first telescope to China in 1630, and carried out regular eclipse observations at Beijing from 1644: these continued until 1785, even though the Church had been proscribed in 1723. Ricci, for all his understanding of Chinese culture, effectively ensured that Chinese astronomy, included its theory of eclipses, could not hold its own against Western science. None the less, the dragons that eat the Sun retained their place in Chinese folklore, as they do to this day.

The Arab World

There are two main sources for eclipse astronomy in the Arab world, one general and the other specific. The former consists of chronicles covering a period of some 700 years, from roughly 800 to 1500, and relating matters, not necessarily astronomical, of historical interest. The actual choice of material was a matter for each individual chronicler, whose task was to compile a record in chronological order and covering a wide geographical area. If an eclipse was recorded, the reason could be that it was seen as foretelling the death of a ruler. Also, in the world of Islam the darkness brought about by a solar eclipse could be seen as a sign to go to the mosque for the *Maghrib*, the prayer recited at sunset (and the fourth of the five daily prayers required of all devout Muslims); such instances are also recorded in the chronicles, and one record[19] mentions a *khutbah*, or sermon, on the eclipse, together with a special eclipse prayer.

The specific record of medieval Arabic astronomy, entitled *Al-Zij al-Kabir al-Hakimi*, was compiled at the beginning of the eleventh century by the Cairo astronomer Ibn Yunus, and contains records of eclipses occurring between 829 and 1004. Those occurring before 933 were observed from Baghdad, and those after 933 from Cairo. Ibn Yunus was himself the observer of most of the Cairo eclipses. His motive in compiling his record was altruistic: he wished simply to make life easy for future astronomers. In addition to Ibn Yunus, other medieval Arabic astronomers recorded eclipses occurring over a very wide area, extending from Turkmenistan and Persia in the east to Egypt in the west: the chronicles also contain eclipse records from what is now Spain.

Ibn Yunus was particularly concerned with accurate prediction, since he had noted that the actual times of the eclipses recorded in Baghdad deviated from the times predicted by methods derived from Ptolemy's *Almagest*. Unfortunately neither Ibn Yunus, nor any other of the astronomers (as opposed to the chroniclers), ever recorded a total solar eclipse. On the other hand, the astonishing accuracy they achieved in measuring the altitude of the Sun (which, given the poor quality of medieval clocks, was the usual means of determining exact times) is clear from the eclipse records. The astronomers, operating in a part of the world with dazzling sunlight, knew well the risks of looking at even a partially eclipsed Sun with the naked eye. They preferred, therefore, to look at the Sun's image reflected in water.

In practice the medieval Arabic astronomers, whose lives were regulated by the Islamic lunar calendar, were more interested in lunar eclipses. What is more, any one lunar eclipse can be observed over a very wide area, with very little variation between the different observations. The only difference is in the local time of the various phases of the eclipse. This means that if the local time can be accurately recorded at two different places, the longitude (east–west) difference between them can be calculated. Once again, the mediocre quality of medieval clocks was a problem, but the results obtained were still remarkably accurate. With the invention in eighteenth-century England of accurate chronometers for use at sea, this method of measuring differences in longitude became popular in Europe during the eighteenth and early nineteenth centuries.

Medieval Arabic astronomers were extremely professional, and if the chronicles can be relied on, the ordinary people of the Arab world were remarkably sober in their reaction to eclipses. This was a period when the achievements of Arabic science far outshone those of the Western Christian world. None the less, when it came to eclipses, Arabic astronomy achieved little beyond increasingly accurate observation. The astronomical theory contained in the *Almagest* was still definitive. From the sixteenth century onwards, when a revolution in astronomy would transform Western science, the Arab world had almost nothing to contribute despite its impressive historical record. Without this revolution the true measure of eclipses could never be grasped.

The New World

Although, in the Old World, each of the different eclipse astronomies examined above made its own distinctive contribution, the different civilisations were in contact with one another from a very early time. None of them had any contact with the New World, where the classic Maya civilisations, centred on the Yucatán Peninsula, recorded in their own distinctive written language thousands of astronomical observations. The records span a long period that began some two thousand years ago. As in Babylon and China, astrology was the sole motive for Mayan astronomy, and because 'the fear engendered by the departure from the regularity of nature epitomized in the eclipse was as real then as is our present fear of nuclear war',[20] accurate prediction was a challenge which the Mayan astronomers could not ignore. Anthony Aveni's definitive study, *The Stargazers of Ancient Mexico*, shows us how successfully they met it.

Unfortunately the Spaniards, when they conquered and settled Mexico and Yucatán in the sixteenth century, destroyed almost all the Mayan records, known as codices, so that today only three or four survive. The most important of these, known as the Dresden Codex (after the European city where it was rediscovered in the nineteenth century), has three pages devoted to eclipses.

Maya chronology, particularly as it relates to eclipses, is far too involved to have a place in the present chapter. Its most distinctive feature was the so-called Tzolkin period of 260 days, which is almost exactly three-quarters of the length of the eclipse year, 346.62 days. This is equivalent to 173.31 days (the interval between conjunctions of the Sun with the two nodes of the Moon's orbit) being equal to two-thirds of the Tzolkin period – so that there are almost exactly three such alignments in every two Tzolkin periods (the discrepancy is less than 2 hours in a period of 520 days). The result is that in a Tzolkin calendar eclipses tend to occur on the same days, such as 7 Ik or 11 Manik, although, as a result of the time discrepancy, the Tzolkin calendar eventually becomes out of sync with the actual passage of time.

The problem with the Maya is that, however good their understanding of eclipses (including their ability to predict them), not a single one of the eclipses now known to have taken place in the classic period is either recorded or predicted in the surviving records.

For all we know, the thousands of documents destroyed by the Spanish conquerors in the sixteenth century may have contained such records – perhaps in greater abundance that those to be found on the cuneiform tablets from ancient Babylon. At the same time, not all Mayan monumental sites have been fully explored by archaeologists, so there is a chance that the 'missing link' will be found. Nevertheless, the material already decoded is sufficient to reveal a civilisation with an unparalleled gift for astronomical observation, including that of eclipses.

5

The Solution from Physics

The revolution in Western astronomy

The eclipse of 11 August 1999 may be seen as a portent for
the end of the second millennium of our era. The beginning
of the millennium, in the eleventh century, witnessed the
start of a process which would lead to the radical transformation of science and technology to the point now reached at
the end of the twentieth century. This chapter represents
an interlude in which this process is described with few
direct references to its relevance to eclipse astronomy; the
rationale is simply that the revolution in astronomy in the
Western world, which reached its climax in the sixteenth
and seventeenth centuries, transformed the way astronomers
would be able to reckon with eclipses. In histories of astronomy, the invention of the telescope, and in particular its use
by Galileo at the beginning of the seventeenth century, are
taken to define the turning point.

Before this transformation, astronomy was above all the
handmaid of astrology and subservient to the dictates of the
Church. The transformation left it a free science, with practi-

98

cal applications (so far as they counted) in fields such as navigation and surveying. There was also a significant change in the use of recorded observations (which, after the invention of printing in the fifteenth century, could be disseminated throughout the international astronomical community). Under the old order, such observations, compiled with ever increasing accuracy, were already an essential research base; this was also their relevance for the prediction of eclipses. Under the new order, the tools of modern mathematics, derived from the study of existing records and the theories developed to explain them, would enable celestial phenomena to be predicted into the indefinite future, and with almost perfect accuracy. This was the point reached in the middle of the eighteenth century, with the publication of the first annual volume of the *Nautical Almanac* in 1766 – a landmark in the history of the use of astronomy for navigation.

The Decline and fall of the old order

Historically, the eleventh century was a turning point. In the preceding centuries the Western world of Latin Christendom was a scientific desert. The world of Islam was in the vanguard of science, and the interface between Islam and Christendom was in Spain, which had fallen to Islam in the eighth century. Christian scholars who wanted to learn serious science had to acquire their knowledge in one of the great Islamic centres of learning, such as Toledo or Córdoba. One such scholar, Gerbert of Aurillac (*c*.945–1003), returned to France to become head of the cathedral school at Rheims, which he was to transform into a widely recognised centre of learning (before going on to spend the last years of his life in Rome as Pope Sylvester II). His return home coincided with the introduction of the astrolabe, an instrument developed by Arabic astronomers for measuring the angle between the horizon and a heavenly body, and indispensable for serious astronomy. In the Western world, astronomy was once more on course to become a mathematical science.

In Spain itself the eleventh century was the period in which the *reconquista*, the process of regaining the country for Christendom, got under way with the help of such romantic figures as El Cid. The fall of Toledo, in 1085, opened one of the world's great intellectual centres to Western scholars. In particular, the *Toledan Tables* compiled by al-Zarqali, once adapted for the longitudes of Western Europe, allowed Western astronomers to calculate the positions of planets for any instant of time.[1] They also set a precedent for the later development, in the sixteenth and seventeenth centuries, of mathematical tables of trigonometrical functions and logarithms, an indispensable resource for astronomers and navigators (now capable of being stored in a hand-held calculator).

One way or another, the reborn Latin world of the second millennium also got its basic astronomical paradigm from the world of Islam, but this was still Ptolemy's *Almagest*, which had been preserved and translated by Arab scholars. The result was that Western scholars worked with a Greek theory (that of Ptolemy) but with Arabic instruments (the astrolabe and the Toledan Tables). Another breakthrough was the introduction of so-called Arabic numerals (which had originated in India some time in the first millennium).

The result, when it came to the prediction of eclipses, was a much increased accuracy – as the Chinese were to discover when Matteo Ricci came to visit them in 1582. At the same time, eclipse astronomy became somewhat marginal. Eclipses were no more than occasional phenomena arising out of alignments of the Sun, the Earth and the Moon occurring, incidentally, in accordance with the information recorded in the tables.

In the end, accuracy, based on ever more exact measurements of celestial phenomena, brought about the downfall of the Ptolemaic world-view – although this involved eclipse observations only indirectly. The key theoretical breakthrough came when the Polish astronomer Nicholas Copernicus (1473–1543) demonstrated that a paradigm based on a planetary system with the Sun at its centre was not only compatible with all the observations based on the Ptolemaic system, but also provided a better explanation for many of them. Essentially, Copernicus achieved his results by developing the purely mathematical consequences of Ptolemaic astronomy to a point where a model of the Solar System with the Sun at its centre proved to represent far more accurately the actual observed positions of the planets. The physical basis of Ptolemy's theory of epicycles was allowed to stand.

In particular, Copernicus's heliocentric (Sun-centred) model placed the orbits of Venus and Mercury inside that of the Earth, so that these two planets would never be visible in the middle of the night, but only in the hours immediately after nightfall or before daybreak. This phenomenon had been noted since the very earliest days of astronomy – several millennia before Copernicus's day – and Ptolemy's geocentric (Earth-centred) model, needless to say, took account of it, but in doing so it had to assume that the periods of Venus and Mercury were both equal to that of the Sun: that is, a year. Copernicus's model did not require this, and allowed the true periods to be calculated. These proved to be seven and a half months for Venus and three months for Mercury – results which fitted both Copernicus's own tables and the astronomical observation on which he had based them. What is more, the same mathematical process enabled the periods of Mars, Jupiter and Saturn to be calculated, and the results showed that the order of the planets from the Sun – Mercury, Venus, Earth, Mars, Jupiter, Saturn – determined according to the length of their periods, was the same as that determined according to the geometry of Copernicus's model. In short, the farther a planet is from the Sun, the longer its period.

In Copernicus's model, the Moon ceased to be a major planet quite simply because there was no need for it to be one. Ptolemy's geocentric model is correct in placing the Moon in orbit around the Earth, and lunar phenomena such as eclipses can be explained equally well on the basis of the Sun also being in orbit around the Earth. It was the comets and planets that dethroned Ptolemy, not the Moon.

The underlying premiss of the Ptolemaic model goes much further back in Greek history. The basic concept was that the Earth was a fixed sphere at the centre of a Universe bounded by the much greater sphere of the fixed stars. Aristotle (384–382 BC) proposed a fundamental distinction between terrestrial and celestial, between nature and cosmos. The former defined the imperfect world of *terra firma*, comprised of the four elements – earth, fire, air and water – in which people lived and died; the latter, the firmament in which the heavenly bodies, composed of the 'quintessential' fifth element, continued indefinitely in their cycles. The weather and other atmospheric phenomena were terrestrial, and belonged to the science of meteorology (from *meteôros*, meaning 'lofty'); this was also the world of comets, and other similar, intermittent phenomena. Endoxus and other early Greeks gradually improved upon Aristotle by locating the Moon and the planets in intermediate spheres, which in some way supported them. This established the essential basis for the Ptolemaic model of planetary motions. Dante's *Paradiso* (the third part of the *Divine Comedy*) is based on this model, which is not surprising, seeing that Thomas Aquinas (1225–74), known for his great respect for Aristotle, had ensured that it became part of the Western Church's official teaching.

In 1577 the Danish astronomer Tycho Brahe, known both for the accuracy of his observations and for his vast catalogue of the stars (which would completely overshadow anything derived from the *Almagest*), observed a brilliant new comet. His observations showed not only that it was located among the planets (so that it had to be celestial rather than terrestrial), but also that its orbit passed right through the celestial spheres which supported the epicycles of the planets. With one blow he had demolished both Aristotle and Ptolemy – or so one would think. In fact, he still had doubts about the implications of his own work.

Without Aristotle's *terra firma*, projectiles sent into the air would not come back to Earth. And if the Earth revolved around the Sun, then the observer's position in relation to the stars would, at the two extreme ends of any diameter of the Earth's orbit (say that defined by the summer and winter solstices) shift by a distance equal to the length of the diameter. Seeing how great this distance is,[2] the observed position of any star should shift significantly as the Earth moved round its orbit. This, the phenomenon of parallax, was not detectable with Tycho Brahe's instruments. Instead of rejecting Aristotle and Ptolemy, Tycho Brahe compromised and modified the Ptolemaic model of the Solar System in a way that took into account his own observations, while at the same time retaining the Earth at the centre of the Universe. The so-called Tychonic system is no more than a curiosity in the history of astronomy; fundamentally it was just as mistaken as the Ptolemaic system from which it derived.

Tycho Brahe spent the last four years of his life (1597 to 1601) in Prague, serving the Emperor Rudolf II. He devoted his time largely to the publication of his observations, but in his last months he was joined by a young assistant, Johannes Kepler (1571–1630), whose work was to revolutionise astronomy by establishing that the science was part of physics rather than geometry. This was also a transition that would ensure that astronomy served practical ends such as navigation (which had become increasingly important with the discovery of the New World at the end of the fifteenth century), rather than esoteric ends such as astrology. This was essentially the beginning of the modern age.

Kepler's first important insight came from his search for an explanation of the fact, discovered by Copernicus, that the outer planets of the Solar System travelled more slowly than the inner planets. (As a first-order approximation, the velocity of a planet is inversely proportional to the square root of its distance from the Sun.) According to Kepler the reason is that the force of the Sun, which drove the planets, would become weaker at greater distances. His pathbreaking *Mysterium cosmographicum*, published when he was only twenty-five, clearly placed the Sun at the centre of the planetary system.

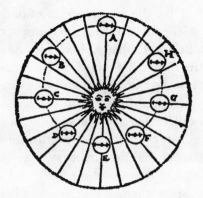

Figure 5.1 Johannes Kepler discovered that Mars has an elliptical orbit, not a circular one. As shown in this illustration from his *Astronomia nova*, he tried to explain this in terms of the Sun's magnetic force acting on the planet, represented here by a small compass.

Kepler arrived in Prague to work with Tycho Brahe in February 1600. The problem he tackled first concerned the orbit of Mars, which, according to a set of ten observations made by Tycho Brahe when Mars was at opposition (when the Earth came between Mars and the Sun in direct alignment), deviated significantly from the circular orbit required by the Ptolemaic model. The deviation was small, but the unprecedented accuracy of Tycho Brahe's observations meant that there was no doubting it. Kepler eventually resolved the problem by placing Mars in an elliptical orbit, with the Sun at one of two foci of the ellipse (as illustrated in Figure 5.1). This is now known as his first law of planetary motion: that all planets move in such orbits.

Having established his first law, Kepler went on to establish the second and third. The second law states that the sector traced out by a planet in the plane of its elliptical orbit in a given period of time has constant area, so that, in effect, a planet moves fastest when it is closest to the Sun. In the language of physical astronomy, the velocity of a planet is at a maximum at perihelion, and at a minimum at aphelion. In 1609, this – together with the first law, and both supported by pages of involved (and often incorrect) mathematical physics – was published in Kepler's monumental *magnum opus*, the *Astronomia nova*,[3] which appeared in 1609. The third law, which was not discovered by Kepler until some years after the publication of the *Astronomia nova*, states that the cube of a planet's average distance from the Sun is proportional to the square of the period of its orbit.

Kepler's three laws are in fact true (at least as a first approximation) for any celestial bodies in orbit. This means that they also govern the orbits of the moons of the Solar System, including that of the Earth, so that they regulate also the occurrence of eclipses. The precise operation of the laws for one particular body is frustrated by the gravitational forces exerted by other bodies in the system. This was the case with Mars, whose orbit is affected by the presence of the other planets in the Solar System. To take this into account requires a second-order correction, but Kepler's observations were not accurate enough to show the necessity for this. A similar correction is required where a planet has more than one moon (as do all the planets, except for Pluto, outside the Earth's orbit); in this case the vast mass of the Sun in relation to those of the planets means that its presence must also be taken into account.

The new order of Western astronomy

It was Kepler who took astronomy out of the realm of geometry into that of physics, and it was an invention made during his lifetime that would ensure the extreme accuracy of the observations needed to support his new theories. In the history of astronomy the invention of the telescope marks a turning point as significant as that of Columbus's discovery of the Americas in world history.

The origins of the idea of the telescope are lost to history. It must have been clear that if such an instrument could be made, with sufficient magnifying power, it would be of inestimable value to astronomy – the branch of science based entirely on the observation of the only non-terrestrial objects known to humankind. The first telescope for which there is satisfactory evidence was constructed in Holland at the beginning of the seventeenth century, in the form of an instrument consisting of a long cylindrical tube with lenses of curved glass at both ends. The insight that led to its invention was simple enough: the distortion of an image, as viewed through one lens, could be corrected by a second lens placed at a suitable distance in the line of sight.

News of the Dutch invention reached the Florentine astronomer Galileo Galilei in the summer of 1609, the year that saw the publication of Kepler's *Astronomia nova*. Within a year Galileo had built a telescope having magnification of 20 with which he made a number of remarkable discoveries. To begin with, while his telescope produced an enlarged image of the planets, it did not do so with the stars. The obvious conclusion was that the stars are much farther away (which also explained Tycho Brahe's failure to detect any parallax). Galileo's next discovery, made in January 1610, was even more revolutionary. Observations of Jupiter over a period of a week revealed that it had four moons. Neither the astronomy of Ptolemy and Aristotle, nor that of Tycho Brahe, could accommodate this new discovery. It was fundamental to the whole regime of epicycles that a planet could not have moons, because they would have to penetrate the planet's heavenly sphere in the course of their orbits. (The Earth, in the old order, did not count as a planet, so there was no problem with the Moon orbiting around it.) What is more, the telescope revealed that the Earth's moon, far from being a perfect sphere (as required by the cosmology of Aristotle and Aquinas), had an irregular surface with mountains and valleys, whose heights and depths Galileo was able to estimate. Even the Sun was observed to be 'spotty and impure'.

With one key insight, Galileo anticipated Newton. Unlike Aristotle, who insisted that physics must explain motion, Galileo insisted that it was acceleration, a change in motion, that required explanation. Movement at a constant speed was a steady state (of which rest was only a special case) and generated no sensation in people who experienced it. This explained why the Earth's inhabitants are not conscious of its speed as it follows its orbit around the Sun. On the other hand, Galileo ignored Kepler's elliptical orbits – although he certainly knew of them. At the end of a confrontation with the Roman Church in 1632, he abjured the Copernican system, and accepted the Earth as the centre of the Universe, but added – according to attribution – one of the most famous quotations in the Italian language, *'Eppur si muove'* – 'it still moves'.

Galileo died in 1642. After his death, the action in astronomy moved to the north of Europe: to France, Holland and, above all, England. In England the importance of modern science was recognised by the founding of the Royal Society, which held its first meeting at Gresham College, in the City of London, in 1660. In 1662 the Society appointed Robert Hooke (1635–1703) as its Curator of Experiments, and in 1665 he became Gresham Professor of Geometry.

In 1666 Hooke demonstrated to the Royal Society an arrangement consisting of a pendulum divided, close to its end, into two parts, each carrying a weight, one of which represented the Earth and the other the Moon; the two weights then not only revolved around each other, but also together revolved round a central point representing the Sun. This model could be extended to any planet, such as Jupiter, which had its own satellite system. There was no reason why it should not apply outside the Solar System, although it was not until the end of the twentieth century that astronomical observation provided evidence that stars might have their own planets. In 1674, Hooke finally presented the theoretical basis underlying his model in the form of three suppositions stated at the end of his 'Attempt to prove the motion of the Earth':

First, That all Coelestial Bodies whatsoever, have an attraction or gravitating power towards their own Centers, whereby they attract not only their own parts, and keep them flying from them, as we may observe the Earth to do, but that they do also attract all the other Coelestial Bodies that are within the sphere of their activity. . . .

The second supposition is this, That all bodies whatsoever that are put into a direct and simple motion, will so continue to move forward in a straight line, till they are by some other effectual powers deflected and bent into a Motion, describing a Circle Ellipsis, or some other more compounded Curve Line.

The third supposition is, That these attractive powers are so much the more powerful in operating, by how much the nearer the body wrought upon is to their own Centers.[4]

As a statement of principle, Hooke's three suppositions would hold their own until Einstein's general theory of relativity would call them into question in the twentieth century. Like Einstein's theory, and unlike any preceding theory, Hooke's three suppositions are remarkable for their extreme generality: no mention is made of particular instances, let alone of the Sun, Earth or Moon. Aristotle's distinction between 'celestial' and 'terrestrial' was consigned to the ash-can.

The picture painted by Hooke is of a system of bodies in space which would all go their own way, in straight lines leading to infinity, were it not for the fact that for any two of them, each was subject to the 'attraction or gravitating power' of the other. This is equally true of any number of such bodies, so that each one of them is subject to the 'attraction or gravitating power' of all the others. However true this may be, the mathematical implications are simply daunting – so much so that to this day no general, exact solution has been obtained for the mutual motions of even three such bodies. None the less, the result (at least before Einstein) is the Universe as we know it.

All is not lost, though. Chaos can be reduced to order by using a procedure well-known to applied mathematicians, for whom it has long been indispensable. It is simply that in a physical system any factor can be treated as negligible, so long as its effect, measured quantitatively, is sufficiently small in relation to other dominant factors. This procedure, as already noted, produces a rough and ready first-order approximation. This may be refined into a second-order, and higher-order approximations by successively taking into account factors that were treated as negligible in earlier approximations. In the end, because any science is based on measurement, successive orders of approximation are useful only if the quantitative modifications which they require can be measured by the instruments available to those carrying out experiments and observations. In the modern age, astronomers – no less than other scientists – tend to allow their mathematics to run ahead of what can actually be observed and measured.

For the Solar System the first-order approximation is based on the principle that the Sun is so large in relation to any of the planets that in any consideration of its effect on one of them, the rest can be ignored. When it comes to the stars, many of which are many times greater than the Sun, these can be neglected simply because they are so far away. The Earth's orbit around the Sun is thus calculated on the basis that the Sun is a fixed point, to which the Earth is attracted by some gravitating power. (This also describes the Moon's position in relation to the Earth, a matter to be returned to later.)

The question is, what is the measure of this gravitating power? Is there some formula for the mutual attraction of two bodies? In 1673, the Dutch physicist Christiaan Huygens (1629–95) had considered the forces acting on a stone swung round on the end of a string. In particular, he wondered, how does the inward pull of the string relate to its length and the speed of the stone? (There has to be some pull to explain the trajectory of the stone once it is released.) Huygens was able to show that the pull was proportional to the square of the velocity divided by the length of the string.

Kepler's third law had already demonstrated that the square of a body in a circular orbit was proportional to the cube of the radius of the orbit. Hooke combined the results obtained by Kepler and Huygens to show that Huygens' pull is inversely proportional to the square of the radius. In 1679, he communicated this result to Isaac Newton in the following words: 'my supposition is that the Attraction always is in a duplicate proportion to the Distance from the Center Reciprocall'.[5] Newton appears never to have reacted to Hooke's letter. But later, in 1684, Newton was visited by Edmond Halley (today famous for the comet named after him), who asked him 'what he thought the curve would be that would be described by the Planets supposing the force of attraction towards the Sun to be reciprocal to the square of their distance from it.' Newton's prompt reply, that the curve would be an ellipse, struck Halley 'with joy and amazement'.[6]

Isaac Newton was born in 1642, the year Galileo died. He became an undergraduate at Trinity College, Cambridge in 1661, but his professional career may be said to have begun when he became a fellow in 1667, to succeed Isaac Barrow as Lucasian Professor of Mathematics in 1669. Until 1696 he remained in Cambridge, but he then moved to London, where for the last 24 years of his life he was President of the Royal Society. Long before he died, aged 84, in 1727, he was internationally acknowledged as one of the greatest scientists and mathematicians in history. To this day, no one has equalled his achievements.

In the early days, when Newton was first confronted with the ideas of Huygens, Hooke and Halley, his own great work, ('*Mathematical Principles of Natural Philosophy*', known familiarly as the *Principia*) was far from his mind. But his exceptional capacity for solving the most intractable problems in physics was already well known. His proof of the elliptical orbit required by the inverse square law was a major breakthrough, since Huygens had been able to prove his law only for a circular orbit – a special rather than a general case. Newton went further, to state a completely general law of gravitation: where two bodies, with masses m_1 and m_2, are separated by a distance r, their mutual attractive force is Gm_1m_2/r^2, where G is the so-called gravitational constant[7] – fundamental not only in Newton's theory of gravity, but also in Einstein's. By the standards of his own day, Newton had found a 'theory of everything', or at least of everything that mattered.

How, then, should Newton's theory be applied to the Solar System, taking into account not only all the planets but also their moons? Newton himself found the prospect daunting:

> But to consider simultaneously all these causes of motion and to define these motions by exact laws admitting of easy calculation exceeds, if I am not mistaken, the force of any human mind.[8]

For a simple system containing only two bodies, Newton was able to prove that both would have elliptical orbits, with their centre of gravity, in each case, being a focus of the ellipse. At the same time the orbit of the body with the greater mass would be smaller than that of the less massive body. In a binary system of, to give a common example, two stars, the respective masses will often be similar, so that both spin about a centre of gravity about half-way between them (in such a case one star may eclipse the other – a phenomenon of considerable interest to modern astronomers). If the mass of one body is many times that of the other, the smaller appears to be in orbit around the larger, as with planetary satellites, for example. In the Solar System,

Jupiter is the only planet whose centre of gravity with the Sun does not lie within the Sun itself, and even then it is only just outside it. When it comes to the Earth, its centre of gravity with the Sun is less than 500 km from the Sun's centre: this is no distance at all, considering that the Sun's radius is 696,000 km, and the Earth's distance from the Sun nearly 150,000,000 km. In short, the Sun's elliptical orbit due to planetary 'action at a distance' is determined mainly by Jupiter, and even so Jupiter's orbit is more than a thousand times larger than the Sun's. Even with the massive size of Jupiter, the Sun, as a first-order approximation, may be taken to be a fixed point at the centre of the Solar System, and as such a focus of the elliptical orbits of all the planets.

The same analysis can be applied to the orbits of the Earth and the Moon around their centre of gravity, which is about 1600 km inside the Earth's surface, some way from its centre. (The Earth's mass, in relation to the Moon, is small[9] compared to that of other planets – ignoring Pluto – in relation to any of their moons.) This makes the first-order approximation rather dubious, with various consequences. In particular the Earth's orbit around the Sun needs to be corrected, while the Moon's orbit around the Earth has to take into account the gravitational pull of the Sun. Newton showed that the Sun's pull reduced the effect of the Earth's gravity when the Moon was either at the point in its orbit closest to the Sun (which occurs at the time of new moon) or at the point farthest away (at the time of full moon). At the quarters, half-way between these two points, the position was reversed so that the Sun's gravitational pull augmented the effect of the Earth's pull on the Moon. That was not all. The Earth, in its elliptical orbit, passes through the points of *perihelion* (when it is closest to the Sun) and apohelion (when farthest away); at perihelion the Sun's gravity reduced the Earth's gravitational attraction on the Moon, while at apohelion the reverse effect would occur. All these results confirmed the observations, of unprecedented accuracy, made and recorded by Tycho Brahe, for which Newton's theory of gravitation provided a complete explanation. Newton's theory of gravity also explained how tides are caused by the Moon's gravitational pull. A complete understanding of the effect of the Moon's gravity on the speed of the Earth's rotation had to wait for research carried out in the twentieth century.

Newton also had a theory to explain a curious anomaly discovered in the 1670s. Using Newton's theory of gravitation, Huygens had shown how the time taken by a pendulum to swing should depend only on its length. Expeditions, funded by the Académie Française, to Lapland (close to the north pole) and Peru (on the equator), showed that the period of a pendulum varied according to latitude, with a minimum at the two poles and a maximum at the equator. Newton showed how the discrepancy (which was very small) would be accounted for if the Earth's radius measured from either pole were less than that measured from any point on the equator.[10] What is more, the flattening at the poles was a result of the Earth's rotation. This provided a complete explanation of the precession of the equinoxes discovered by Hipparchus, more than 1800 years before the time of Newton.

What has all this to do with eclipses? First and foremost, the celestial mechanics established by Newton was sufficient, in principle, to determine the exact orbits of all the planets and their moons in the Solar System. In practice, Newton's theory of the Moon's orbit, as set out in 1713 in the second edition of the *Principia*, still contained errors of detail – the factors governing the Moon's orbit were simply too complex. None the less, Newtonian mechanics established, once and for all, the principles that would govern the occurrence of eclipses, whether of the Sun or the Moon. All that remained was simply to sharpen the theory to take into account the discrepancies noted in the Moon's orbit by observers in Newton's own day.

Solving the problem of the discrepancies in the Moon's orbit was critical, for Newtonian theory in principle provided a means for determining longitude at sea by measuring the distance between the Moon and a suitable reference star. At the time, the greatest problem in navigation at sea was the accurate measurement of longitude. What navigators needed were accurate and reliable tables of lunar positions; such tables, following from the work of Tycho Brahe, already existed for stars.

The problem was not solved in Newton's lifetime. The theory necessary for a solution was provided by Leonhard Euler (1707–83) – one of the greatest mathematicians in history. A German astronomer, Tobias Mayer (1723–62), used Euler's theory to produce tables of lunar positions. These he sent to London in 1754, hoping to win a share of the £10,000 prize offered by the British Board of Longitude for any practical method for the accurate determination of longitude at sea. The testing of Mayer's tables was delayed by the Seven Years War (1756–1763), but once tested they proved to be accurate enough to qualify for a share in the prize, £3,000 going to Mayer's widow, and £300 to Euler. Mayer's lunar tables made possible the publication of the first official *Nautical Almanac* in 1766, an annual publication which has appeared ever since, with tables for both the Moon and the stars.[11]

The *Nautical Almanac* was the essential base for the canons of the eclipses that began to appear in the nineteenth century. Eclipses, whether of the Sun or of the Moon, had become completely demythologised – at least in the scientific world. Newtonian mechanics, as refined by Euler and represented in the tables of the *Nautical Almanac*, had reduced eclipses to no more than a minor phenomenon. This was to prove a blessing in disguise. Although the prediction of eclipses was possible long before the eighteenth century, the unprecedented accuracy of the *Nautical Almanacs* encouraged the organisation of scientific expeditions to observe them wherever and whenever they might occur. The nineteenth century would show physics moving out of Newton's world of celestial mechanics and optics, and into a new world focused upon the actual processes and interactions, physical and chemical, taking place within the stars. The Sun was much the nearest star, and its occasional eclipse by the Moon provided an unprecedented opportunity to observe it, together with any number of phenomena associated with it. Solar physics, rather than celestial mechanics, would be the name of the game.

6

The Gateway to Discovery

The great English eclipse of 1715 and its aftermath

The solar eclipse of 3 May 1715 (during which London experienced more than three minutes of totality) not only covered almost the whole of the south of England, but also allowed Edmond Halley (one of the greatest of all British astronomers) to record the space and time coordinates of such an event with unprecedented accuracy. As the locations recorded on Figure 6.1 show, Halley had arranged in advance for reports to be made, not only from six points on the edges of the path (which was 304 km wide), but also for nine more (including the Greenwich Observatory) within it.

This can be taken to be the beginning of modern eclipse astronomy. The information sent to Halley – who already had accurate measurements of the Moon's diameter – enabled him to calculate that of the Sun with unprecedented accuracy. Modern research, relating Halley's records to the advances in the positional astronomy of the Sun and the Moon made since his time, have led not only to small corrections in the path of totality (as Halley recorded it), but also

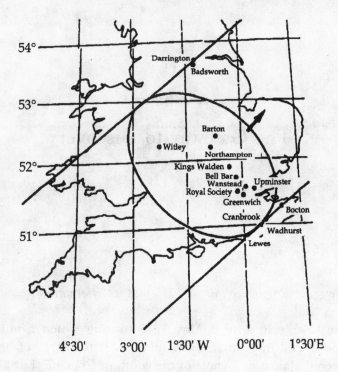

Figure 6.1 The 3 May 1715 eclipse: the path of totality, the dimensions of the lunar shadow and the places from where observations were made.

to a discussion, among today's experts, as to whether there has been a small change in the diameter of the Sun since 1715.[1]

Now, at the end of the twentieth century, astronomers still follow solar eclipses, making observations relating to diverse phenomena. Some, working in fundamental astronomy, compare timings from terrestrial observations with those made from Global Positioning Satellites.[2] Others monitor changes in the atmosphere or the appearance of the shadow bands.[3] The methods, and above all the technology, were unknown until long after Halley's day. This chapter describes three separate areas in which the solar eclipses have proved to be indispensable to the work of astronomers in the course of the present century.

Solar physics and the corona

Until well into the nineteenth century, the scientific world accepted what the French philosopher of science, Auguste Comte (1798–1857), had to say in 1835 about celestial objects: that 'never by any means, will we be able to study their chemical composition, their mineralogical structure, and not at all the nature of organic beings living on their surface'.[4] If Comte was right, then, with the observations of celestial phenomena enshrined in the *Nautical Almanacs*, astronomy had more or less reached the end of the road. But calculations based on Newton's celestial mechanics would soon lead to the discovery of the eighth planet, Neptune, in 1846. The seventh, Uranus, had been discovered in 1781 by William Herschel, who was simply looking at the right part of a sky through a telescope, but Neptune represented 'the ultimate triumph of Newtonian dynamics'.[5] And by 1846, two other events had occurred that would change the whole course of astronomy.

The first was the independent discovery, by William Hyde Wollaston (1766–1828), an Englishman, and Joseph Fraunhofer (1787–1826) a German, both working at the beginning of the nineteenth century, of dark lines crossing the spectrum of sunlight (which had first been investigated by Isaac Newton). Fraunhofer achieved his results by filtering the sunlight through a very narrow slit before it passed through his prism. He used a telescope to examine the hundreds of lines that then became visible, and counted some 600. This technique then became standard in astronomy, together with the classification of the divisions in the spectrum defined by the darkest and most prominent lines. Starting at the red end of the spectrum, Fraunhofer labelled these with the letters of the alphabet from A to H, although he himself failed to discover the significance of the lines themselves.

The second event was the invention of photography. The Frenchman Louis Daguerre (1789–1851) played a key role when, in 1839, he produced a successful image on a photographic plate. Things then moved very rapidly. On 8 July 1842 the crescent Sun was photographed during the phases of partiality both before and after the total eclipse of that date – the first successful eclipse photographs in history. In 1843 a successful daguerreotype was made of the spectrum of the solar photosphere – the main source of the Sun's light. On 28 July 1851 a similar success was achieved at Königsberg, with a daguerreotype of the total solar eclipse – the first ever obtained during the period of totality. The image was recorded in time to be displayed at the Great Exhibition in London that year.

By this time, the development of railways, steamships and the electric telegraph had begun to revolutionise transport and communications, so that in the second half of the nineteenth century, astronomers and others were able to travel to almost every corner of the world to observe solar eclipses. Why, it must be asked, did they hardly ever miss a chance to do so? To answer this question, we must look again at the science of spectroscopy (as it developed from the days of Wollaston and Fraunhofer), and its role in discovering both the chemical composition of the Sun and the physical processes taking place within it. For this research the opportunities for observation provided by solar eclipses were indispensable, for only then was it possible to observe the Sun's corona. Needless to say, this, the most spectacular of all eclipse phenomena, visible only during totality, must have been observed by *Homo sapiens sapiens* throughout the whole period of the species' existence. The first clear reference to the corona, by Kepler in his *Astronomiae pars optica*, suggests that he saw it as belonging to the Moon.[6] It was only in the nineteenth century, that it was to become the main focus of interest among eclipse astronomers.

The corona, consisting of ionised gases (the precise definition of which will come later in this chapter), is the turbulent outer atmosphere of the Sun, extending into a space to several times the Sun's own diameter. As such it was ideally suited for spectroscopic analysis. In ordinary daylight the dazzling light of the Sun comes from the photosphere, its visible bright surface, which emits photons – the basic particles of light – in a steady stream which takes some 8.3 minutes to reach the Earth. The photosphere is then (except for the Sun's atmosphere) its outer layer, which, although only 500 km deep (and so representing no more than 0.1 per cent of the Sun's radius), is our main source of sunlight. The corona, although its temperature is several hundred times that of the photosphere, is much less bright, and emits mainly heat. The light it does emit is much more accessible to both direct observation and photography than is the photosphere, provided that it does not have to compete with the photosphere's intense light. It is because it shields the photosphere and reveals the corona that a total eclipse of the Sun is a key event is solar physics.

From the time of the Königsberg eclipse of 1851, observation of the corona – whether direct, spectroscopic or photographic – has continued, from one solar eclipse to another, for nearly 150 years. Photographs of the corona constitute an illustrated history of solar physics during this period; they have never ceased to amaze both astronomers and public.

With solar eclipses, the importance of high-quality photographic equipment (which is nowadays often a digital camera, whose images are displayed on a computer screen) comes from the fact that the photographs themselves can only be taken during the few minutes – never as many as eight – of totality at any particular place. Such an opportunity occurs at most seven times in a decade, so that a few minutes of intensive work represents the climax to months of preparation. The contrast with stellar astronomy, continuing throughout the year with the help of massive telescopes in observatories located at sites (such as Mauna Kea in Hawaii) selected for optimal atmospheric conditions, could hardly be greater. Solar astronomers do have the advantage, however, of the proximity of the Sun (which is 250,000 times closer to the Earth than even the nearest star) so that magnification and the resolution of images is no great problem. In fact, far more is known from observations of the Sun than from any other star.

For the first hundred years of professional eclipse expeditions, the equipment was bulky, and the observers – who would have spent days, if not weeks, travelling to their destination – would set up a whole camp with support from locally recruited labour. In the present jet age, eclipse tourists work with compact equipment and generally stay in hotels. In the 150 years since Königsberg one factor has not changed: the requirement for good weather. Even today, a whole expedition can fail if clouds hide the eclipsed Sun and the corona during the few minutes of totality.

What have travelling eclipse astronomers been trying to discover over the last 150 years? In the nineteenth century, and well into the twentieth, they were mainly concerned with confounding Auguste Comte by discovering the chemical composition of the Sun. This is where spectroscopy came in. Although Fraunhofer now takes most of the credit for the discovery of the dark lines in the solar spectrum that are now named after him, their true significance was not discovered until a generation after his death. In 1859 Robert

Bunsen (1811–99) and Gustav Kirchhoff (1824–87), working together in Heidelberg, announced the discovery, based on laboratory experiments, that each chemical element had its own distinctive set of Fraunhofer lines. This enabled Bunsen and Kirchhoff to deduce the existence of two new elements, caesium and rubidium, by identifying Fraunhofer lines not corresponding to any known element.

In contrast to Fraunhofer's work with sunlight, the lines revealed in the laboratory were light, not dark. The explanation for this phenomenon was that light was *emitted* by each element at the wavelengths corresponding to the lines, whereas the dark lines observed by Fraunhofer represented light at wavelengths *absorbed* in the Sun's atmosphere. The distinction is fundamental: the starting point for laboratory spectroscopy is light *emitted* at certain wavelengths, whereas that for solar spectroscopy is *absorbed* at certain wavelengths. This is, however, no more than a starting point: as will become clear later, emission lines from both the corona and the layer beneath it in the Sun's atmosphere, the so-called 'chromosphere', play an important part in solar physics.

The problem in the laboratory is to produce the light required for spectroscopic analysis from the different chemical elements involved, which is easier said than done since in normal conditions they do not emit light. An element must either be made incandescent by heating it to a sufficiently high temperature, or be used as a pole in an electric arc (as used in welding). In either case, the light produced must not be mixed with that from other elements, if an accurate spectrum for the elements test is to be produced. Once this is achieved, however, then the laboratory spectra can be used to make a table of the wavelengths of the distinctive emission lines for each element, which can then be used to decode the absorption lines detected in light from the Sun and, on a more sophisticated level, the emission lines in light from the chromosphere and the corona.

Well before the end of the nineteenth century, astronomers using spectroscopy had detected some fifty elements in the Sun. This represented a breakthrough from laboratory physics into astrophysics – a milestone in the history of astronomy. In the process, the observation of the Sun during the period of totality of a solar eclipse played a key role. The first major eclipse to attract international interest was that of 8 July 1842, which astronomers observed from several locations along the path of totality as it crossed southern Europe. These observers were struck not only by the white corona, but also by three prominences, of a colour best described as red tinged with lilac.

Curiously, at this early stage there was still some doubt as to whether the corona and the red prominences actually belonged to the Sun rather than the Moon, but doubt was dispelled by observations taken at two different points – 400 km apart – along the path of totality of the solar eclipse of 18 July 1860. These results were confirmed by eclipse observations in 1869 and 1870.

The eclipse of 15 November 1868, observed from India, provided the first experience of the so-called flash spectrum. Just before second contact, the spectroscope focused on the eclipse suddenly revealed hundreds of bright lines, and when the phenomenon was observed again at the eclipse of 22 December 1870 it was realised that the wavelengths of these emission lines were the same as those of the dark absorption lines of the photosphere (such as are normally detected by normal spectroscopic analysis of sunlight). Already, in 1868, two astronomers, the Frenchman Jules Janssen and the Englishman Norman Lockyer, had noted that the light from the solar prominences, as observed in the spectroscope, contained a bright orange line which, although similar to the orange lines of the sodium spectrum, did not belong to it. The brightness of the light refracted through the spectroscope during the Indian eclipse of 18 August 1868 gave

Janssen the idea for a new design of spectroscope which would enable the unexplained orange line to be studied in light from the photosphere, without having to wait for the few minutes of totality of a solar eclipse. This led him to the discovery of a new element, named 'helium' from the Greek work, *hēlios*, for the Sun. Helium is now known to follow hydrogen at the beginning of the periodic table of elements. It is also, after hydrogen, the second most common element in the Universe, and as such accounts for 27 per cent of the Sun's mass. (Although it was only in 1895 that it was first found on Earth, it is now widely used both in research and for practical applications, such as providing the lighter-than-air gas used in Richard Branson's balloon.) All in all, the 1868 eclipse, for starting the process which led to the discovery of helium, can be regarded as the highpoint in the history of eclipse astronomy.

The real mystery came not with helium, but with coronium, an element identified as a result of analysing flash spectra recorded from eclipses. The period from the first observed 'evidence' for the existence of coronium until the final explanation of its non-existence lasted nearly fifty years, and at the turn of the twentieth century this particular chimera was at the centre of eclipse astronomy. What, then, did it all add up to? And what new understanding of the corona and the chromosphere followed from clearing up the mystery, a result only finally achieved in 1942?

Following the eclipse of 7 August 1869, which was visible over much of North America, spectroscopic observations of the corona revealed, in increasing measure, Fraunhofer lines not corresponding to any known element. Throughout the 1880s, eclipses observed in different parts of the world – Egypt, Micronesia and the West Indies – brought to light more and more unexplained coronal lines. After nine had been photographed during the West African eclipse of 1893, a new element, 'coronium', was conjured up as the only possible explanation. Observations in later years appeared to provide confirmation, and after results obtained at the eclipse of 29 June 1927 there were sixteen unexplained lines. Astronomers still had nothing but coronium to explain them.

The solution came indirectly as a result of another unexplained element, for which Fraunhofer lines were observed in the spectra of nebulae, interstellar gas clouds far outside the Solar System. This could not be coronium because the lines were simply not the same, and the observations in no way depended on solar eclipses. The obvious explanation was another new element, dubbed 'nebulium'. The problem was that, with the advance of physics in the early years of the twentieth century, there was little room left in the periodic table of elements (which then ended with uranium, with atomic number 92) for two new ones.

The real explanation came as a result of fundamental research by the Danish physicist Niels Bohr (1885–1962), who used the new quantum physics, in which he was a leading figure, to explain the Fraunhofer lines. Like so many advances in science, Bohr's discovery came from noting a parallel between two apparently unrelated phenomena. The first was the discovery by an otherwise unknown Swiss mathematics teacher, Johann Balmer (1825–98), that all the Fraunhofer lines related to frequencies of light equal to a constant multiple[7] of

$$\frac{1}{a^2} - \frac{1}{b^2}$$

where a and b are both whole numbers. Later, the Cambridge physicist John Nicholson (1881–1955) noted that, within an atom, 'the angular momentum of a particle can only rise and fall by discrete amounts when electrons leave or return'. What this meant to Niels Bohr was that the 'discreteness of spectra was the consequence of the discreteness of atomic states',[8] and the link between the two was Planck's constant, h^9 (discovered by the German physicist Max Planck (1858–1947) in 1900, and long established as one of the most fundamental quantities in physics).

If we are not quite home, we are (thanks to Bohr) well on the way. The basic atom of any element consists of a nucleus of protons and – except for hydrogen – neutrons. The number of protons is the atomic number; the combined number of protons and neutrons is the atomic weight. A listing of elements in order of their atomic number constitutes the so-called periodic table, which is now (at the end of the twentieth century, but not at the beginning) completely filled from 1 (hydrogen) to g2 (uranium). Beyond that lie unstable elements not found in nature which were first created in the laboratory; by 1998 the end point lay at element number 113. The protons each carry a unit positive charge of electricity, and the nucleus is surrounded by an equal number of electrons, each carrying an equivalent negative charge. The electrons are to be found in a number of different orbits (depending on the particular element), and the basis of quantum phenomena is largely to be found in the movement of electrons either from one orbit to another, or out of the atom altogether.

It is this latter case that is critical for astrophysics in general, and the deconstruction of coronium (and nebulium) in particular. Atoms of all elements can lose electrons, some more readily than others. By losing a negative charge, an atom gains an equivalent positive charge. It is said to become ionised, and the atom itself becomes an ion. An ion always has more energy than the un-ionised atom. It also means a different mix of the numbers a and b in Balmer's equation, and a different set of Fraunhofer lines in the spectrum.

In principle, the process of ionisation can continue until an atom has lost all its electrons, so that it becomes an ion with a positive charge equal to its atomic number. Iron (Fe), for example, with atomic number 26, would become, in principle, a positive ion with a charge of 26 if it were to lose its entire negative charge, represented by its 26 electrons. The iron atom in its normal state, designated Fe I, has no positive charge. With the loss of one electron, it becomes Fe II (with a positive charge of 1), and so on to the upper limit of Fe XXVII (with a positive charge of 26). This is the end of the road, which it will never come close to reaching in practice, since even the hottest stars do not generate the energies appropriate to this level of ionisation.

Since the whole of molecular chemistry (actually a pleonasm) depends upon electron bonding, each successive stage in the process of ionisation makes everyday chemistry increasingly problematical. Much of the matter in the Universe has a very high temperature and is therefore highly ionised. Matter that consists almost entirely of highly ionised atoms is in a state called plasma – also known to physics as the fourth state of matter. Plasma, needless to say, is not part of everyday life on Earth (which exists at temperatures far below that of any plasma), but it does comprise the greater part of all stars, including the Sun.

The photosphere, which is the outer layer of the Sun, we now know to be a plasma. The chromosphere and the corona are conventionally referred to as the Sun's atmosphere. In the early twentieth century it was not appreciated what high temperatures prevailed in the Sun's atmosphere, and it was assumed that the corona and the chromosphere should behave like a gas, not a plasma. The problem about coronium was that if it was one of the elements, the emission lines in its spectrum would be 'forbidden' under the ordinary laws of quantum physics.

In 1927 the Californian physicist Ira Bowen showed that emission lines in the spectrum of a star, Nova Pictoris – which at the time could have been taken as evidence for nebulium – were actually caused by ionised oxygen. In 1933 a nova in the constellation Ophiuchus exploded, and five 'coronal' lines were observed in its spectrum – thus undermining the distinction between coronium and nebulium. This gave the Swedish physicist Bengt Edlén the idea that the key 'red' line observed in the spectrum of the corona could be Fe X. Following this up, he saw that nineteen of the coronal emission lines could similarly be explained in terms of highly ionised atoms of calcium, iron and nickel. It was not until 1941, however, that the German astronomer Walter Grotrian produced a theoretical proof of Edlén's hypothesis as it related to Fe X. In step with the theoretical requirement for increased energy with every successive stage in the ionisation process, this would be possible provided that temperatures in the corona were sufficiently high. Fe X, if it were to account for the observed emission lines, would have to exist at a temperature of a million degrees Kelvin – which would mean in practice that the corona was not a gas but a plasma.

This is still more or less the present state of the game. Spectroscopic observations of the corona going back to the middle of the nineteenth century have established, beyond any reasonable doubt, that it is far hotter than could possibly be explained by any theory then prevailing. Originally these observations were possible only from shortly before second contact to shortly after third contact in a total eclipse of the sun. Edlén's conclusion, based on Fe X, has stood the test of time for more than half a century. It was the result not only of the most important work in eclipse astronomy, but also of some of the greatest insights, notably those of Niels Bohr, in the history of twentieth-century physics. This is not the end to what can be discovered from observing the corona during a solar eclipse, but the balance of the book would be lost if the subject were to be pursued any further. It is time to move from the quantum physics of Niels Bohr to the general relativity of Albert Einstein.

The general theory of relativity

It is popularly believed that Einstein, with his general theory of relativity, dethroned Newton. This is overstating the case. To this day Newton's theory of gravity is still more than adequate to explain the celestial mechanics of the Solar System. But there are phenomena that only Einstein's theory explains. There were two questions to be answered: what were these phenomena, and how were they to be observed?

But first, something must be said about the background. The first full statement of Einstein's general theory, in impeccable scientific guise, appeared with the title 'Die Grundlage der allgemeinen Relativitätstheorie' in the *Annalen der Physik*,[10] the leading German journal in the field of physics. In the international scientific world it did not help that the paper was published in the middle of the First World War, when Einstein was working in Berlin.

In the 'Grundlage' (which simply means 'foundation'), Einstein tacked a problem which had never really worried Newton. Gravity, as Newton saw it, was simply a force operating instantaneously over limitless distances, and satisfying the laws he had formulated. Einstein saw gravity as a property of matter itself, with effects which had to be transmitted across contiguous portions of spacetime. What is more, gravity would also affect light, so that it could no longer be accepted that light emanating from a given source would travel to its destination along a straight line. This is what led Einstein to introduce the concept of the 'curvature of space', which right from the beginning has caused a good deal of confusion.

We have already seen how the scientific breakthrough represented by the celestial mechanics of Newton was the result of his substituting a physical approach – expressed in his law of gravity – for Ptolemy's essentially geometrical approach. Newton did not reject geometry: he simply took the established geometry of Euclid for granted, and where necessary improved upon it. None the less, it was no more than background.

Einstein, in a sense, returned to Ptolemy and looked for a geometrical foundation for his theory. He found it in the work of a German mathematician, Bernhard Riemann (1826–66), whose masterpiece *On the Hypotheses which Determine the Foundations of Geometry*,[11] showed how Euclidean geometry depended ultimately upon a set of axioms, and that these could be dispensed with provided that another self-consistent set was substituted for them. By doing just this Riemann established a non-Euclidean geometry, which was not based upon the straight lines fundamental to Euclidean geometry. (This explains why mathematicians describe as 'curved' any space whose geometry is not Euclidean, although this is misleading since it is not the space but its geometry that is curved.) Einstein saw that there was nothing in space that required Euclidean, or any other sort of geometry: after all, geometry, at the end of the day, is a mental construct. He was looking at space from a new perspective: the question was whether, in doing so, he could explain phenomena that Newtonian physics could not account for.

The high-precision observations which became possible in nineteenth-century astronomy led to a problem about the observed motions of the planet, Mercury. Quite simply, the perihelion of Mercury – the point in its orbit closest to the Sun – was observed to advance by a specific amount each year. Some idea of the accuracy achieved by the astronomers is provided by the fact that the rate of advance was no more than 43" (43 seconds of arc) per century. Since Mercury completes its orbit in 88 days (equivalent to a little more than four times per Earth year) a little arithmetic will show that the perihelion requires some 12.5 million completed orbits to return to the same place. None the less, nineteenth-century astronomers were deeply worried by the anomaly, and put forward any number of ingenious ideas to explain it. Einstein dismissed all of them, when he noted that the discrepancy 'could be explained by means of classical mechanics only on the assumption of hypotheses which have little probability, and which were devised solely for this purpose'.[12] In other words, Newtonian mechanics had lost the battle with the advancing perihelion of Mercury. Einstein's general theory did, however, explain the discrepancy. Applying his own equations, Einstein showed that the perihelion of Mercury should advance almost exactly 0.1" for every completed orbit. With 420 such orbits in a century, this gives 42" – almost exactly the figure derived from the observations made in the nineteenth century.

The objection to accepting Einstein's explanation of the advance of the perihelion of Mercury was that it dealt with a phenomenon that had long been known to astronomy. In short, the theory could have been contrived simply to fit known facts (which is quite legitimate, but makes the theory somewhat less compelling). If Einstein's general theory was to be established once and for all, it would have to predict the results of observations yet to be made. This is where the total eclipse of the Sun comes in.

The Netherlands remained neutral in the First World War. Einstein was able, therefore, to send a copy of his article in the *Annalen der Physik* to a Dutch professor of astronomy, Willem de Sitter, who sent it on to the Royal Astronomical Society in London. The Society's President, Arthur Eddington, responded by asking de Sitter to write an article, in English, about the general theory for the Society's *Monthly Notices*. This de Sitter did, noting in his article that the general theory not only 'explains the anomalous motion of the perihelion of Mercury', but also 'predicts a number of phenomenon [sic] which have not yet been observed'.[13]

De Sitter's article was noted by the Astronomer Royal, Sir Frank Dyson, who had long had a special interest in solar eclipses. He realised that if light, as Einstein suggested, was subject to gravity, then it would pay to make a special study of the stars visible in the immediate neighbourhood of the eclipsed Sun during the few minutes of totality. The light from these stars, passing close to the Sun, would be strongly influenced by its gravitational field. This would show up on photographs as slight changes in the stars' positions when compared with photographs of the same stars taken when the Sun was in a quite different part of the sky. Dyson first played his hunch by studying photographs of the eclipse of 30 August 1905, taken from Sfax in Tunisia, but they could not help him.

The solar eclipse expected on 29 May 1919 could solve the problem, since the Sun would then be among the bright stars of the Hyades cluster, in the constellation Taurus. Early in 1917, with the end of the war, already in its third year, hardly in sight, Dyson, in spite of the fact that he was out to prove a theory originating in the enemy capital, persuaded the British government to grant £1000 to fund two expeditions to observe the 1919 eclipse. One (led by Eddington) would go to Principe, an island off the coast of West Africa, and the other to Sobral, in north-east Brazil – both locations on the path of totality. By the beginning of 1918 preparations were well under way, even though the war was still far from over.

A series of photographs taken from the Greenwich Observatory in January 1919 placed the Hyades in a reference frame of other stars. These would then be compared with the pictures to be taken during totality. In the event, the Principe observations had to contend with clouds which hid the Hyades, but even so there was one plate which, on examination, produced results that confirmed Einstein's theory. Eddington, all of whose doubts were dispelled, described this as the greatest moment of his life. The Sobral expedition did even better: the main set of seven photographs taken there all confirmed Einstein's calculation of the expected deflection of the light from the Hyades.

The process of returning the photographs to London and analysing them took time. Einstein himself heard of the results in a telegram sent on 27 September by the Dutch physicist, Hendrik Lorentz (1853–1928), a colleague of de Sitter and a close collaborator of Einstein at the beginning of the century. In a letter which followed on 7 October, Lorentz thought the results obtained from the two eclipse expeditions to be 'certainly some of the most beautiful results that science has produced and we should indeed rejoice'.[14]

The official announcement was made by the President of the Royal Society, J. J. Thomson (who had discovered the electron in 1897) at a joint meeting with the Royal Astronomical Society held at Burlington House, London, on 6 November 1919. The meeting attracted immense interest. In his opening speech, Thomson described Einstein's theory as 'one of the greatest achievements in the history of human thought . . . the greatest discovery in connection with gravitation since Newton enunciated his principles'. Dyson's own report recorded that 'the results to the expeditions to Sobral and Principe leave little doubt that a deflection of light takes place in the neighbourhood of the Sun and that it is of the amount demanded by Einstein's generalised theory of relativity as attributable to the Sun's gravitational field'. It is doubtful whether eclipse astronomy will ever again achieve a result of such cosmic importance. The philosopher A. N. Whitehead, who had also attended the meeting, later described how

the whole atmosphere of tense interest was exactly that of a Greek drama. We were the chorus commenting on the decree of destiny as disclosed in the development of a supreme incident. There was dramatic quality in the very staging – the traditional ceremonial, and in the background a picture of Newton to remind us that the greatest of scientific generalisations was now, after more than two centuries, to receive its first modification. Nor was the personal interest wanting; a great adventure in thought had at last come home safe to shore.[15]

With hindsight, we are entitled to ask how far the hype of 1919 was justified. First, at the risk of spoiling the party, we must note that as far back as 1804 a German astronomer, Johann Soldner, not only suggested that light rays could be deflected by the Sun's gravitational field, but went on to calculate the amount of the deflection. The basis of Soldner's theory was Newton's corpuscular theory of light, which suggested that the corpuscles, although infinitesimal in size, would still have a mass and therefore would be subject to the Sun's gravity. Soldner, whose work was unknown to Einstein, calculated a deflection of about half that predicted by Einstein. His work was not followed up by further research in astronomy, and his result is no more than a historical curiosity.

Returning to the twentieth century, the procedure adopted at the 1919 eclipse was repeated by teams of observers in Australia (21 September 1922), Sumatra (9 May 1929), the USA and Japan (19 June 1936), Brazil (20 May 1947), Sudan (25 February 1952) and Mauritania (30 June 1973). None of the results obtained would have restored Newtonian theory, and all confirmed Einstein, or would have done so, had not a new theory entered the lists in the 1960s – by which time Einstein himself had been dead for several years. The so-called Brans–Dicke theory introduced a new quantity, the 'scalar field', into the Einstein equations for the gravitational field. The amended equations gave a value for the deflection of starlight by the Sun that was 8 per cent less than that predicted by Einstein's theory. None of the solar eclipse observations ever achieved the necessary accuracy to settle the conflict between Brans–Dicke and Einstein either way. In the end, two radio astronomers, A. B. Fomalont and R. A. Sramek (making no use at all of eclipses), rescued Einstein with the help of observations carried out in 1974 and 1975, but offered something of a reprieve to Brans and Dicke by noting that 'the difference between the Brans–Dicke theory and general relativity are slight for most physical applications'.[16]

Finally, for Einstein the fact that sunlight would be deflected by the Sun's gravitational field meant that the fundamental particles, or photons, by which light was transmitted should have a mass equivalent to their 'specific energy' (as determined by their frequency). The consequences, as noted by J. B. Zirker, are bizarre. According to the general theory, the mass of a body tends to infinity as its velocity approaches that of light. In the so-called standard model of modern particle physics, both photons (the energy quanta of light waves) and gravitons (the energy quanta of gravity waves, which transmit the gravitational force) have a rest mass of zero. This means that they offer no resistance to changes in their motion, so that Einstein's definition of what he rightly called the *equivalent* mass of photons (which by definition move at the velocity of light), corresponding to their 'specific energy', can still hold.

As to the graviton, Gerard 't Hooft – a world-ranking figure in particle physics – accepts its existence only because

> it appears to be an inevitable consequence of the theories of gravity and quantum mechanics . . . It has never been detected, however, and we do not expect to see it in the foreseeable future.[17]

As we approach the 1999 eclipse, things seem to be less certain than they were in 1919.

The Earth slows down

We now move on to something quite different, and get our feet back on the ground. Geophysics is the name of the game. This subject, as its name suggests, represents the interface between physics and geology. As such it is important to oil and mineral prospectors, and others who wish to probe the hidden depths of the world. In one very specialised area, geophysicists look for possible changes in the rate at which the earth rotates on its own axis. The field is led by Richard Stephenson of the University of Durham, who in 1997 published a massive, expensive and absolutely fascinating book, *Historical Eclipses and Earth's Rotation.*[18]

Ptolemy was probably the first astronomer to note that the length of the solar day varied according to the seasons. Now, at the end of the twentieth century, days are longest towards the end of October, and shortest at the beginning of February: the difference is about 50 seconds, in a mean solar day of 86,400 seconds. This is a little less than 0.06 per cent – not enough to worry about, but a very large discrepancy in comparison with that which Einstein sought to explain when he considered the advance of the perihelion of Mercury. (In fact the Earth's perihelion also advances, though by much less than Mercury's, and this may also have a microscopic effect on the length of the day over very long periods of time.) The varying length of the day over the course of the year, as discovered by Ptolemy, follows mainly from two separate causes: the ellipticity of the Earth's orbit, and the tilt of its axis at an angle of 23° 27', to the ecliptic. (The tilt is the reason for the variation respective in the hours of night and day according to the seasons).

Ptolemy never considered the possibility that the length of the mean solar day (the average length of the day over the course of a year) might itself vary over a period counted in hundreds if not thousands of years. Plainly, the length of the solar day depends upon the Earth's rate of rotation, which itself determines the number of solar days in a year. If, therefore, the Earth slows down, then solar days will become longer, and their number in the year will be reduced. If the Earth speeds up, the reverse will happen.

It seems likely that Leonhard Euler (whom we have already met) was the first to suggest – in a letter to a bishop – that the day might be growing shorter. In any case, in 1754 the Prussian Royal Academy of Sciences offered a prize for solving the following problem:

> Whether the Earth, in its rotation round its axis, by which it brings about the alternation of night and day, had undergone any alteration since the first period of its origin. What may be the cause of it, and what can make us certain of it?[19]

Both questions are answered in Stephenson's book, but first we must look at some of the intervening history. The well-known German philosopher Immanuel Kant (1724–1804), in the same year as the prize was offered, suggested that the tides caused by the gravitational attraction of the Sun and Moon would, by moving the waters of the oceans in a direction opposite to that of the Earth's rotation, slow down. This, if true, would mean that days would become longer, contrary to what had been suggested by Euler.

Kant's theory of the tidal retardation of the earth's spin was basically correct, and tidal friction is now accepted as the major long-term cause of variation in the length of the mean solar day. The difficulty facing Kant and his contemporaries was that of finding a practical means of either proving or disproving the theory. For one thing (as the English astronomer William Herschel noted in 1781), the problem with investigating possible variations in the period of the Earth's rotation was

> the difficulty of finding a proper standard to measure it by; since it is itself used as the standard by which we measure all the other motions ... It is perhaps not altogether impossible but that inequalities may exist in the (diurnal) motion, which, in an age where observations are carried to such a degree of refinement, may be of some consequence.[20]

Herschel suggested various means of overcoming the obstacles to measuring the length of the day (such as comparing it to the rotational periods of other planets), but they came to nothing, mainly for want of sufficiently accurate clocks and chronometers in the eighteenth century.

Nearly a century before Herschel's day, Halley had concluded from his study of ancient records of eclipses that the Moon was accelerating in its orbit around the Earth. What he failed to realise was that the observed effect, as deduced from the old records, was caused in part by the Earth slowing down – the phenomenon which Kant was to suggest in 1754. Somewhat surprisingly, astronomers treated the acceleration of the Moon in its orbit and the retardation of the Earth's rotation as unrelated phenomena until well into the nineteenth century. In 1866 the French astronomer Emanuel Liais pointed out that

> By the law of mechanics, a reduction in the speed of a celestial body causes a recession such that the 'angular movement' is increased. Thus there exist [both] a real acceleration of the motion of the Moon and an apparent

acceleration arising from the increase in the length of the day.[21]

The extreme complexity of the actual mathematical relation between the two quantities means that the two phenomena, in practice, must continue to be investigated independently of each other, correlation of the results leading to refinements of the equations. This does not, however, rule out a short if simplified explanation of why the gravitational effects of the Moon on the Earth, and vice versa, are the main cause of both phenomena.

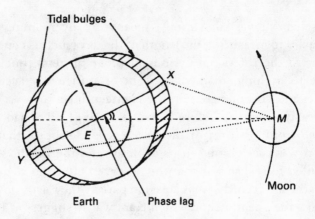

Figure 6.2 The tidal interaction between the Earth and the Moon. XY is a diameter at the Earth's equator.

Figure 6.2 is an illustration of the tidal interaction between the Moon and the Earth. For simplicity it is assumed that the oceans cover the whole of the Earth's surface (as recounted in Chapter 7 of the Book of Genesis). If the water in the seas were perfectly fluid, then at any given moment there would be bulge in the oceans reaching its highest level at the point where the Moon is directly over-head. The oceans on the other side of the world will then have a corresponding bulge with its high point at the other end of the Earth's diameter from the high point directly under the Moon. (Given the inclination of the Moon's orbit in relation to that of the Earth's equatorial plane, this point will always be within, or close, to the tropics.) In practice, the viscosity of sea-water means that the effect of the Moon's gravity is delayed, so that the bulges take some time to reach their maximum height; the Earth will by then have rotated on its axis, creating a phase lag, as shown in Figure 6.2. Seeing that the half of the oceans above the line ME is on balance closer to the Moon than the half below the line, it will be more susceptible to the attractive force of the Moon's gravity. The net effect of this force is then to retard rather than to accelerate the Earth's rotation. At the same time, following the principle established by Liais, the Moon will accelerate in its own orbit. The historical record of eclipses, for what it is worth, makes possible the study, over two or three millennia, of both phenomena – the former in relation to solar, and the latter in relation to lunar eclipses.

The basic principle is the same in either case. Although the mathematical equations underlying the *Nautical Almanacs* (and other astronomical tables which predicted the state of the heavens into the indefinite future) are modified from time to time to keep in step with the latest observations of the motions of the Moon and the planets (and the state of the art in astronomy which they reflect), this process has not been carried backwards into the era of the historical records of eclipses which interest geophysicists. The reason for not doing so is simply that the conclusions drawn from these records constitute at least one factor which the modified equations must take into account. (Other relevant factors, which enormously complicate the equations, are the geographical variations in the physical parameters of the oceans – depth, temperature, density and so on – and the landmasses which cover about a third of the Earth's surface.)

Although today's geophysicists have computer programs for establishing the time and space coordinates for eclipses, both solar and lunar, when it comes to past eclipses the mathematics incorporated into the programs is the same, in principle, as that used in the nineteenth century by Theodor von Oppolzer, whose *Canon of Eclipses* lists the time and location of historical eclipses, calculated on the assumption that the Earth's rotation has *not* slowed over the historical period considered (which means, also, that the Moon did *not* accelerate in its orbit). The process of calculation can be continued back into the indefinite past, determining for every total solar eclipse not only an exact geographical location for the path of totality, but also the local time at which every point on the path experienced totality. At this stage the geophysicists put on their historical hats, and compare the computer results with those gleaned from the historical records.

Stephenson shows what we can learn from such comparisons. The basic principle is illustrated in Figure 6.3, which relates to the total solar eclipse observed from Babylon on 15 April 136 BC. This particular eclipse is chosen because it is described in remarkable detail on two cuneiform tablets now in the British Museum. In the figure, the left-hand curved line is a computer reconstruction of the path of totality, based on the assumption that, over the years since 136 BC, there has been no change in the rate of the Earth's rotation. The right-hand curved line shows where the path would have been, according to modern geophysical theory, if the tidal effects described above were the only force affecting the rate of the Earth's rotation. The fact that the actual path of totality, to pass over Babylon, fell short of this line means that some other geophysical effects must have acted

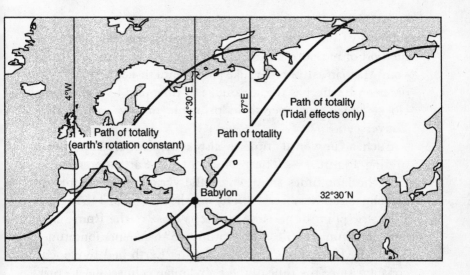

Figure 6.3 The eclipse of 15 April 136 BC.

to counteract the tidal friction. What these might be is a matter considered at the end of this section.

To avoid confusion at this stage, a point already made in Chapter 2 must be repeated loud and clear. The time and space coordinates of any eclipse, lunar or solar, looked at from any point outside the Earth's surface, depend neither on the rate of the Earth's rotation nor on the actual face of the Earth presented to the Sun at any moment during the eclipse. If you were an astronomer on Mars, with all the equipment necessary to observe the orbital motions of the Earth and its Moon, and possessed a knowledge of late-twentieth-century astronomy, you would understand exactly when, where and how eclipses occur without needing to know anything about the Earth's rotation. This is a subject for geophysics, not astrophysics. As a Martian astronomer you would have to have some way of measuring the passage of time which did not depend upon the Earth's rotation, but

– as Herschel discovered in the eighteenth century – the rotation of one planet provides an extremely cumbersome method of measuring time on another. We can assume that your Martian astronomer, like any twentieth-century astronomer on Earth, has the advantage of time told by a caesium clock, which can operate in principle in any part of the Universe.

Such a 'universal' time is also indispensable for interpreting Figure 6.4. The rotation of the Earth determines only the longitudes from which the various phenomena of an eclipse can be observed. During the eclipse of 11 August 1999, the point of greatest eclipse is close to the Romanian city of Rîmnicu-Vîlcea at latitude 45° 6' N and longitude 24° 22' E. If the rate of rotation of the Earth had remained constant since the time of the Babylonian eclipse of 15 April 136 BC, then the point of greatest eclipse in 1999 would still have the same latitude, but its longitude would be 48° 45' east of Rîmnicu–Vîlcea, so that this point would be at 45° 6' N and 73° 7' E; the nearest town would be Chiganak in Kazakstan – nowhere near as accessible for eclipse tourists as Rîmnicu-Vîlcea. At the same time there would be an eastward shift of the same amount for the whole path of totality, and for the different zones of partiality. Imagine rotating the globe portrayed in Figure 6.4 clockwise, through an angle of 40° 24', while the time–phase grid of 'eclipse coordinates' stays still. The path of totality would then cross the south and not the north of France; it would miss out the British Isles entirely, so that Devon and Cornwall would enjoy no more than 80 per cent partiality, and the north of Scotland no more than 60 per cent. The most northerly point on the path would be somewhere near the border between Russia and Ukraine, instead of somewhere in the Atlantic a few hundred kilometres south-west of Ireland.

What interests the geophysicists is the difference, ΔT, between the computed and recorded time of an eclipse. If

Figure 6.4 The eclipse of 11 August 1999, showing the path of totality. The 'time-phase grid' shows the time at which the eclipse will be seen from various locations, and the degree of partiality visible on either side of the central track.

(following the cuneiform records) Babylon had been on the centre-line of the path of totality on 15 April 136 BC, then the difference in longitude, 48° 45' from the computed path, gives value for ΔT of +11,700 seconds of time (since in one hour the Earth rotates through an angle of 15°). The figure for ΔT may well be greater or less than 11,700 seconds, since

145

the records from Babylon nowhere indicate whether the city was central or near to one of the edges of the path of totality. Taking this into account, ΔT is found to be between 11,210 and 12,140 seconds. This means that the mean annual discrepancy in time (calculated over a period of 2130 years) is something over 5 seconds per year. On the basis of the Babylonian records from 136 BC, this defines the secular rate by which the year grows longer.

This is all very well, but these are not the only ancient and exact records of solar eclipses. What if other records lead to conflicting results? One of the historical geophysicists' main preoccupations is to establish the degree to which ancient records, from a number of different parts of the world and from different periods in the history of pretelescopic astronomy, can be relied upon for determining the rate at which the world is slowing down. It is essential to appreciate that these records provide scientific data not available from any other source. Stephenson and his colleagues are in no sense amateur scientists: just read his book.

Stephenson's 'Index of Eclipse Records'[22] lists about 150 pre-telescopic solar eclipses from four different regions or cultures: Arab, Babylonian (including Assyrian), Chinese (including Japanese and Korean) and European (including Alexandrian). After establishing, with meticulous care, criteria for evaluating the accuracy of ancient eclipse records (and therefore their usefulness for geophysics), Stephenson devotes the final chapter of his book to establishing the secular development of ΔT from records going back nearly 3,000 years.

This leads to two significant conclusions: the first is that the secular rate at which the Earth is slowing down has been decreasing over the period of the records. The mean annual rate of increase in the length of the day (which can now be measured with a caesium clock) is therefore also slowing down. The second conclusion comes from relating the curve in Figure 6.4 to the values for ΔT to be expected if tidal friction, as first suggested by Kant, acts on the rotation of the Earth in accordance with the state-of-the-art theory (which is not derived from eclipse observations). In fact, tidal friction theory requires consistently higher values for ΔT, so that if both the theory and Stephenson's analysis of the historical records of solar eclipses are correct, there must be forces counteracting the effect of tidal friction.

This is the view accepted by today's geophysicists, who have made various suggestions as to what these forces might be. They could be the result of post-glacial uplift, a process which would go back to the end of the last ice age, some 10,000 years ago. With the weight of polar ice (which then extended to cover most of Britain) steadily decreasing, the Earth, relieved of the pressure, could have rebounded so as to become less flattened. This so-called 'viscous rebound' would not need to go very far to counteract the effects of tidal friction. At the same time, there may have been significant changes in global sea-level – one of the results expected by doomwatchers to be caused by the greenhouse effect. Geophysics so far lacks the necessary measurements to prove the case either way.

The game is not yet over. As Stephenson, in his characteristic laconic style, notes at the end of his book, 'The investigation of long-term changes in the rate of rotation of the Earth using historical observations thus raises a number of geophysical issues which await further development.'[23]

7

The Problem of Time and Space

'There is no other use for astronomy
than the determination of time'

KAN SAZAN[1] (a Japanese Confucian scholar)

The Earth, the Sun and the Moon as clock and calendar

Fifty-odd years ago, one of Britain's best-known cartoonists, Fougasse, drew a cartoon showing a notice with the words 'OUT OF ORDER' hung on a sundial. This was clearly absurd. Although the sundial, as an everyday timepiece, had been obsolete for centuries, it was obviously still 100 per cent reliable. A sundial out of order could only mean that the mechanics of the Solar System, which provides both the clock and the calendar for everyday life on Earth, was itself out of order. What, then, is the order of time as established and regulated by the Solar System?

One problem, right at the start, is that the passage of time is inevitably measured and recorded by individuals observing celestial phenomena from a base, on planet Earth, which is itself part of the timekeeping system. It was only in the twentieth century that scientists first discovered a means of measuring time that does not require the construction of some regulating mechanism. The new atomic clocks rely on vibrations within the atom, which have exactly the same frequency throughout the Universe. From such a cosmic perspective the division of time into years, days, hours and so on, based on the motion of bodies in the Solar System, may appear to fall by the wayside, but all clocks – including atomic ones – have to be calibrated so as to record the passage of time in the units of time familiar to us. The latest, state-of-the-art atomic clock, the caesium clock, still tells the time in hours, minutes and seconds.

This is perhaps just as well. The appendix 'Astronomical Constants' in W. M. Smart's *Textbook on Spherical Astronomy* contains the following information:

Length of the day
Mean sidereal day = 23^h 56^m $4^s.091$ mean solar time
Mean solar day = 24 3 56.555 mean sidereal time[2]

This leads immediately to the question of how the hour is to be defined, if there are not 24 hours in a day. If this is not confusing enough, the appendix goes on to list the lengths of five different types of month – synodical, tropical, sidereal, anomalistic and nodical – and four types of year – tropical, sidereal, anomalistic and eclipse. The lengths given for the month and the year are referred to the year 1900, with the clear (and correct) implication that the figures for, say, the year 2000 will be different, so that we are left in some doubt about the meaning of the word 'Constants' in the appendix's heading. The Appendix fails to note whether the days in which the different lengths of months and years are measured are mean sidereal days, mean solar days or some other sort of days. And yet, in the late twentieth century all talk about eclipses and many other phenomena to be observed in the skies, such as the conjunctions of planets and stars, proceeds on the assumption that there is complete certainty about the exact times that such phenomena actually occur. Eclipses, in particular, are now located precisely in time and space,[3] so the eclipse of 11 August 1999 should have no surprises in store. How is this to be reconciled with the apparent confusion in a standard textbook on spherical astronomy, first published in 1931 and now in its sixth edition?

Let us return to the distinction between sidereal time and solar time, and look at the two concepts in terms of two propositions, both of which would seem to be self-evident.

(1) The Earth completes one rotation on its own axis in the period of one day.

(2) The period of one day is the time between one instant at which the Sun, observed from some fixed point on the Earth, reaches its zenith (highest point), and the next such instant.

Proposition (1) has a sting in its tail, because the time the Earth takes to complete either one rotation on its axis, or a number of rotations that can be counted, still has to be reckoned in terms of some other measurable period of time. The simple, intuitive answer, is to follow proposition (2), and assume that in the interval of time between two successive passages of the Sun ('transits') across the meridian (which is defined by the direction of the Sun when it reaches its zenith) the Earth has rotated on its own axis through an angle of 360°. The measurement of this interval of time has been a standard procedure at observatories since the time of Tycho Brahe some 400 years ago. All that is necessary is an instrument called a transit circle, which is no more than a telescope mounted so as to point in the direction of the Sun's zenith at midday, with its only freedom of movement in the vertical plane – that is, it can move up and down but not sideways. The transit circle at Greenwich, which dates from 1850, is precisely aligned in the direction of the Greenwich meridian.

A moment's thought shows that the assumption made

above in following proposition (2) must be false. To make things simple, assume that the Earth's orbit around the Sun is a perfect circle, and that there are no variations in the rate at which it rotates on its axis. (Although both these assumptions are false, they are acceptable approximations for the present line of argument.) It is already immediately apparently that in the interval of time (equal to one solar day) between successive transits of a meridian (say that of Greenwich) by the Sun, the Earth must have rotated through an angle greater than 360°. The reason is simply that in that interval of time it has moved on in its orbit around the Sun, by such a distance that in the course of a year it completes a whole orbit. The direction followed by the Earth in its orbit around the Sun is the same as that in which it rotates on its axis – anticlockwise as viewed from above the north pole. In the course of one revolution around the Sun, the small daily increments will add up to a whole rotation of the Earth, so that in principle a sidereal year is exactly one solar day longer than a solar year.

As a unit of time the sidereal year is preferred by astronomers, since its definition, in principle, does not depend upon observations made from a fixed point on the Earth (such as Greenwich). The solar year is essentially pre-Galilean, because it is based upon the principle that the Sun transits – that is, *moves* across – the meridian, whereas the Sun's transit is of course a consequence of the Earth's rotation on its axis.

The sidereal year needs a reference point. This is the function of the so-called 'first point of Aries', denoted by ♈. It was originally defined, some 2,000 years ago, as the point (which then happened to lie in the constellation Aries, the first sign of the Zodiac) where the Sun is at midday on the day, 21 March, of the vernal equinox.[4] Precession (described on p. 54) has now carried this point into Pisces, but somewhat confusingly its name has not been changed.

For an observer on the equator the Sun will then be directly overhead at midday, as its path across the sky changes from the southern to the northern celestial hemisphere.[5]

The effect of precession is to move ♈ along the ecliptic through an angle of 50.3" each year. Astronomers deal with this by defining as a *tropical year* the interval between successive passages of the Sun through the first point of Aries. The *sidereal year* is then derived from the tropical year, by correcting for the 50.3" annual movement of the first point of Aries.

The accuracy now attained in the prediction and recording of eclipses (and all other celestial events such as transits and occultations) goes far beyond the first-order approximations assumed in the explanations given above. The previous chapters of this book mention any number of small discrepancies in the motions of the Sun and the Earth, all of which are going to have some effect on the measurement of the passage of time for as long as this measurement is based on the celestial mechanics of the Solar System. Twentieth-century astronomy has tackled the problem by introducing, first, Ephemeris Time (ET) and then, in 1984, Terrestrial Dynamical Time (TDT) – which in 1991 became simply Terrestrial Time (TT).

The unsatisfactory nature of mean solar time provoked few reactions until well into the twentieth century. Although he was not the first to call for reform, the then Astronomer Royal, Harold Spencer Jones, proposed a workable system in an article which appeared in 1939.[6] Some idea of the precision involved can be gained by looking at the eventual recommendation made by the International Astronomical Association in 1952:

In all cases where the mean solar second is unsatisfactory as a unit of time by reason of its variability, the unit adopted should be the sidereal year at 1900.0; that the time reckoned in these units be designated Ephemeris Time; that the change of mean solar time to Ephemeris Time be accomplished by the following correction:

$$\Delta T = 24.349 + 72.3165\ T + 29.949\ T^2 + 1.821\ B\ \text{sec}$$

where T is reckoned in Julian centuries[7] from 1900.0 January 1 Greenwich Mean Noon and B has the meaning given by SPENCER JONES in *Monthly Notices, R.A.S.* **99**, 541 (1939); and that the above formula also defines the second.[8]

The practical implementation of this recommendation came in 1960, when the International Conference on Weights and Measures defined one ephemeris second as 1/315 569 25.9747 of the length of the *tropical year* for 1900 January 0 at 12 hours Ephemeris Time. On this basis, the length of an ephemeris year would be 365 days, 5 hours, 48 minutes, 45.9747 seconds. This period, although in very close accordance with the accepted rules for defining leap years, was – because of all the small discrepancies – exactly right only for the base year 1900, when the second was of precisely the defined length at 12 noon on 1 January. For all later times, the correction ΔT had to be applied to find the exact ET at any given instant. At the end of the twentieth century, ΔT has grown to just over a minute in relation to 1900.

In spite of its extraordinary accuracy, the definition of the second in terms of ET was to be superseded, some seven years later, by one which for the first time in history had no basis in the celestial mechanics of the Solar System. Following the suggestion by the atomic physicist Isidor Rabi (1898–1988) in 1945 that atomic resonances could be used in a chronometer, the first atomic clock – the caesium beam resonator – was developed in 1955. Its accuracy proved to be far superior to that of any Solar System clock, and in 1967 the second was redefined as

the duration of 9 192 631 770 periods of the radiation corresponding to the transition between the two hyperfine
levels of the ground state of the caesium atom 133.[9]

This is the definition of the second in the internationally
adopted SI system of units.

All astronomical events, both inside and outside the Solar
System, could thus be timed without reference to a standard
defined by the dynamics of the system itself. For the first
time in history, therefore, astronomy could work with a
definition of time that is not essentially circular. In 1971 a
new international standard, based on the SI second and
known as International Atomic Time (TAI), was chosen.
It was defined so as to give the same readings as ET at 0 h
on 1 January 1958,[10] when (according to the 1900 base-line
for ET) $\Delta T = 32.184$ seconds. This quantity then defined the
difference between TAI and the new Terrestrial Dynamical
Time (TDT) which in 1984 replaced ET, and was defined
so as not to produce any discontinuity with ET in 1958.
TDT essentially continues the old regime, while TAI represents the new, subject to the ΔT margin as fixed in 1958.
Since 1984 the two regimes have kept so closely in step that
no aberrations have been observed. Given the extraordinary
care taken with the definitions given above, this is no more
than what was to be expected.

What does all this have to do with observing and recording
eclipses? Why is ΔT, which according to present estimates
will be 64.6 seconds on the day of the 1999 eclipse, so important, when it measures a gain of less than a second a year
from the 1900 base-line? The answer is that the cumulative
effect of one second of time, when applied to the Earth's
rotation, is considerable. In one second a point on the
equator travels 464 metres, so that a ΔT of 64.6 seconds
represents a distance of nearly 30 km. Even at the British
latitudes of totality for the 1999 eclipse (approximately

50°N) the distance is nearly 20 km. This is the correction that the astronomers have to make to take into account the fact that the uniform rate of the Earth's rotation used to determine the ephemeris longitudes they work with does not accord with reality. In terms of longitude, the margin of error arising from non-uniform rotation requires, for 11 August 1999, a correction of 16.2'.[11]

Remarkably in a book about eclipses, the present chapter has yet to say anything about the part played by the Moon. This omission is a result of this chapter's essentially modern perspective. It must be clear, from what has already been said, that from this perspective, there are only two essential questions to be answered: what is the length of the day, and what is the length of the year? In terms of celestial mechanics, these questions relate to two basic phenomena: respectively, the rotation of the Earth on its axis, and its revolution in its orbit around the Sun. Variously interpreted, the first defines the length of the day and the second that of the year. The fact that the Earth happens to have a moon in orbit around it is pretty much irrelevant to these two definitions: this chapter, up to the present point, could have been written equally well from the perspective of either of the two planets inside the Earth's orbit, Mercury and Venus, neither of which has a moon. However, the Moon does have a slight relevance because of its marginal effect on the rate of the Earth's rotation, considered at some length in Chapter 6.

Modern astronomy uses a temporal and spatial frame of reference for the Solar System which is based on the mechanics of the Earth and the Sun (so that, for example, one astronomical unit is defined as the mean distance between the two). When looking at the Moon, and phenomena such as eclipses in which the Moon is involved, it must be fitted into this frame of reference. This proves to be quite complicated but most of the hard work has already been done, either in Chapter 2 or earlier in this chapter in relation to the Sun.

Just as the Earth orbits the Sun, so does the Moon orbit the Earth. The period of the Moon's orbit around the Earth – a month, whose length in days varies according to the appropriate definition – is a fraction (somewhat less than a twelfth) of that of the Earth's orbit around the Sun. The second factor is that the plane of the Moon's orbit around the Earth is inclined at just over 5° to the plane of the ecliptic – the plane of the Earth's orbit around the Sun.

Just as the definition of the sidereal year is based upon the time taken by the Earth to return to a fixed point in the heavens, the first point of Aries, so also the sidereal month is defined by the Moon returning, at the end of a complete orbit, to a fixed point. In principle one should, at this point, take into account the difference between a sidereal and a tropical month corresponding to that between a sidereal and tropical year (which is explained on page 152). Such a difference, however, adds up to less than 7 seconds, whereas that required to derive the tropical from the sidereal year is more than 20 minutes. Even allowing for the fact that there are 13.37 months in one sidereal year, the correction required in the case of the year is proportionately much larger.

The importance of the sidereal/tropical distinction is that it allows like to be compared with like, so that if confusion is to be avoided, at least by astronomers, it is convenient to reckon on the basis of 13.37 (sidereal) months in one (sidereal) year. This, however, only adds to the confusion for the rest of us, reckoning as we do on the basis of a 12-month year (give or take a few days). For an ordinary observer at any given place, the month begins anew with every new Moon (which is also the principle of every lunar calendar, such as the Islamic calendar.) However, in the $27\frac{1}{3}$ days of a sidereal month, the Earth moves in its own orbit around the Sun through an angle of about 27°; the Moon must therefore continue in its orbit through the same angle to reach the same phase as seen from the Earth. This requires another two days or so, so that the length of the so-called synodic month is 29.53 days. This is important for solar eclipses, which can only occur at new Moon, so that the time that elapses between any two solar (or, for that matter, lunar) eclipses is always an exact number of synodic months. On this basis, there are 12.37 synodic months of 29.53 days in a tropical year of 365.24 days; this is equivalent to 12 (synodic) months falling nearly 11 days short of a tropical year. With the Islamic lunar calendar this means that any given month occurs, in every solar year, 11 days earlier in the calendar. This becomes particularly significant when it comes to the ninth month devoted to the fast of Ramadan, which can thus fall in any season of the solar year. With combined lunar and solar calendric systems, such as that of the traditional Chinese calendar, the anomaly is resolved by introducing, generally at three-year intervals, an extra *intercalary* month. This is important for modern scholars seeking to identify the exact date of recorded eclipses, but for the correct understanding of eclipse cycles what is needed is the basic numerical relationship between the different cycles of the Earth and the Moon.

This brings us to the most critical of all such cycles, the regression of the line of the nodes – the line joining the points at which the Moon's orbit intersects the plane of the ecliptic. Because an eclipse can occur only when the Sun, the Earth and the Moon are in alignment, an eclipse year is defined as the interval between two such alignments in which the same node is pointing towards to the Sun. This is a period of 346.62 days. The fact that it is some 18.64 days shorter than the sidereal year is due to the regression of the nodes as explained in Chapter 2. As shown there, the eclipse year is a major factor – though not the only one – in determining the intervals at which eclipses occur.

Finally, the speed of light must enter into the equation. This is very nearly 300,000 km per second, so that light from the Moon, which is on average 384,000 km from the Earth, takes 1.28 seconds to reach us. In this period of time the Earth has rotated through an angle of 19.2", which, in 1999, will mean that the path of totality across south-west England, at a latitude of some 50°N, is some 380 metres to the west of what it would be if the speed of light could be disregarded. This distance, although very small in relation to the length of a parallel of latitude at 50°N, is still large enough for astronomers (with instruments of unprecedented accuracy) to take into account in fixing the coordinates of the eclipse.

Einstein and the cosmic perspective

Equipped now with a caesium clock, we can look at the whole system through the eyes of a divine watchmaker – the perspective of modern astronomy. Suppose that we picture the Solar System as contained in a cosmic box, so that everything relating to it, according to observations made from some point on the Earth, is seen from inside the box. It really does not matter how large the box is, as long as it is large enough to contain the Solar System. Whatever its size, observers inside it will see on its inside surface the familiar stars and constellations. In whatever direction they look this will provide the backdrop for events occurring inside the box – and by definition these events will involve only bodies belonging to the Solar System.

These events will include eclipses, both lunar and solar. However, these eclipses, observed from any arbitrary point within the box, will phenomenologically speaking be nothing more than alignments of the Sun, the Earth and the Moon, to be noted in terms of space and time coordinates with no

fixed origin on Earth. One can envisage a Martian astronomer working on this particular phenomenon, with an
approach comparable to that of Earth-bound astronomers
observing eclipses of the moons of Mars, for example. The
Martian astronomer would be working with other units of
measurement, derived no doubt from the length of the Martian year and the planet's distance from the Sun. But with
that caesium clock ticking away somewhere, and the velocity
of light a physical constant, those units would be some fixed
multiple of those familiar to us on Earth.

Although, as a result of space probes and other state-of-
the-art methods of getting under the skin of Mars, even the
least sophisticated of us now know that there is no possibility
of intelligent life existing on that particular planet, everything in the previous paragraph remains true. We do not
need a real astronomer on Mars – a virtual astronomer will
do just as well. The virtual astronomer does not need to be
on Mars either: any other point inside the box would do
just as well, provided we know its coordinates.

According to Einstein, the box is essentially Newtonian,
for Sir Isaac had to have a space 'at rest' – without it, acceleration would be a magnitude without any meaning. In argu-
ing the case against Newton, Einstein points out that, to
begin with, 'our concept of space has been associated with
the box'.[12] He then looks at what would happen if the thick-
ness of the walls of the box were reduced to zero (which is
entirely legitimate, since the box – at least after the dethrone-
ment of Ptolemaic astronomy – is purely conceptual anyway). The result is that the space within the box becomes
part of some much larger space. For Newtonian mechanics
not only would this larger space have to be confined within
some larger box, but the smaller box would also have to be
at rest within the larger one. This necessity was repugnant
to Einstein's theory, which required the two spaces to be
free to move with respect to each other.

159

That is not the end of the matter because, as Einstein went on to say, 'it must now be remembered that there is an infinite number of spaces, which are in motion with respect to each other. The concept of space as something existing objectively and independent of things belongs to pre-scientific thought, but not so the idea of the existence of an infinite number of spaces in motion relatively to each other.'[13] In this infinite number of spaces, in which all the walls of all possible boxes have melted away, eclipses of the Sun and Moon in one small corner of the Universe count for next to nothing. Einstein accepts that 'general relativity has gone further than previous physical theories in relinquishing "closeness to experience" of fundamental concepts in order to attain logical simplicity.'[14]

The problem is that the whole fascination of eclipses for humankind comes from their 'closeness to experience': with the shadow of the Moon racing across the ground, an astronomical event comes down to Earth in a way quite outside our normal experience of the Solar System. It is no wonder, then, that eclipses became part of the complex of factors involved in the measurement of time outlined in the first part of this chapter. Einstein would have had no problem with the caesium clock, but all the complexities involved in sidereal and synodic months were never part of his Universe (nor are they part of the Universe studied by the vast majority of contemporary astronomers – they are, quite simply, in a different ball-game). Having consciously 'relinquished closeness of experience' Einstein hopefully recognised the irony of his most important theoretical results being confirmed by the close observation of a series of solar eclipses – which would actually continue long after his death.

Paradoxically, the 'closeness of experience', or rather the accuracy with which it can now be measured, is a major factor in explaining the importance of eclipses in modern astronomy. The same is true, although perhaps to a lesser extent, of conjunctions of planets, or of planets and stars. These are all events which have been recorded over an extremely long time-span – in the case of lunar eclipses going back to the cuneiform records of ancient Assyria. As we have already seen from the work done by geophysicists in determining changes in the rate of the Earth's rotation, the historical record can be an important source of scientifically useful data. And the results obtained by using these data can then be used to date, more exactly, historical events recorded as coinciding with eclipses, conjunctions and so on.

Now, at the close of the twentieth century, discrepancies between the predicted space and time coordinates of eclipses and what is actually observed can provide not only the means for correcting the existing equations (which are already extremely complex), but also a basis for new theory. The margins may be microscopic, but we have seen from the use made of the solar eclipse photographs of 1919 that even microscopic differences can be of cosmic significance. None the less, no world-shattering theoretical advance is expected from the 1999 eclipse.

Eclipses and the domestication of time

The psychological basis of time is to be found in the association between the experience of an event and the recollection of similar events in the past. We have no difficulty with placing the succession of days in the framework of time, since each dawn repeats, in all its essential attributes, all past dawns we have experienced. It may well be that the very young child, before it has learnt to talk, has already made this association; this has almost certainly been researched by one developmental psychologist or another. In practice the results of such research do not matter very much, since all humans learn to place repetitive events, such as the dawning of a new day, within a cultural framework long established in the society in which they grow up. The individual child, in this, as in so many other cases, is saved the trouble of reinventing the wheel.

In the majority of cultures, this framework has established the measurement of time according to three astronomical phenomena: the rotation of the Earth on its axis, the Moon's orbit around the Earth and the Earth's orbit around the Sun define, respectively, the day, the month and the year. The practical problem is arithmetical: neither the number of days in a month or a year, nor the number of months in a year, is a whole number. As we have already seen, the length of the month makes it particularly awkward to place in any systematic calendar. The fact that calendars, keeping more or less in step with the cycles of the Earth and the Moon, have existed for thousands of years has required adjustments to be made to the actual astronomical record for reasons of pure expediency. (This may include political expediency, which explains for example why July and August both have 31 days.) No astronomical sophistication is required to recognise the anomalies in the lengths, in days, of the twelve months of the Roman calendar which we still use today. On the other hand, the labour involved in getting things exactly right, for modern astronomy, is immense, as indicated in the first part of this chapter.

Establishing a yearly calendar which is more or less correct astronomically, so that recurrent events such as the helical rising of a particular star always occur on the same day, contributes nothing to the solution of two essential problems in the mastery of time. The first is to find a satisfactory means for counting years; the second is to divide up the day into smaller units of time. Both problems must be solved if records of eclipses, whether part of an oral folk tradition or recorded in writing, are to be of any use. If it were otherwise, not only would the people who made the original records have failed to come to grips with required timekeeping, but the records themselves would defy interpretation by posterity.

The typical scenario of folk tradition is extremely problematic when it comes to eclipses. Even a pre-literate culture must come to terms with events which, although they recur, do not do so according to any fixed rule within its own time framework. An example of such an event is a flash of lightning; whenever one occurs, it can be immediately related – in the cognition of those who experience it – to previous instances. It may be that there is some local 'ethnoscience' containing a theory about the appearance of lightning flashes, relating them, say, to natural phenomena characteristic of certain seasons of the year.

Imagine, then, a population inhabiting a part of the world with no history of thunderstorms, where, suddenly, there is a flash of lightning.[15] There will be no word for the event, and no precedent in any sort of folk memory. The local culture would be in shock, and could deal with the event only as a 'one-off' which, hopefully, would never be repeated. In the course of time, and for so long as the event were retained in the folk memory, people would come to realise that it had no significant long-term or even short-term consequences. Once this happens, the event would probably disappear from the folk memory, for tradition is essentially functional in what it retains. Almost beyond doubt, this has occurred countless times when it comes to solar eclipses; the only trouble is that we have no record of the process. The same scenario would be quite different in a literate culture, for the ability to record the event would at the same time 'domesticate' it. What is more, it is characteristic of such cultures that they have solved both the problems mentioned above: how to count years, and how to divide the day into smaller units of time.

As for counting years, we are so accustomed to working from a fixed origin in time – such as the beginning of the Christian era – that we fail to realise that this system was unknown, even in the Christian world, before AD 525 (when a monk, Dionysius Exiguus, used it in his Easter tables) and did not become widespread until some 500 years later. (The implications of the fact that the Roman Empire had counted the years since the foundation of Rome apparently took a long time to dawn on Christians.) The extension of the Christian system to the years before Christ (BC) had to wait upon the chronological researches of a second Dionysius, Dionysius Petavius (1583–1652), who lived some thousand years after the first. All the dates for the ancient world used in this book are therefore the product of research into historical chronology carried out in the last four hundred years. This is important because, even with the help of the records, the occurrence of a solar eclipse in the ancient world did not immediately establish the length of time that had elapsed since the preceding one.

If such information were known (as it must have been for the secret of the Saros series to be discovered) it would have been quite insufficient to establish any regularity in the occurrence of eclipses. This makes it all the more remarkable that accurate prediction of eclipses occurred so early in history, in both the Middle East and the Far East – and, most probably, in the ancient Mayan cultures of Central America.

In practice, two methods, often combined with each other, evolved for recording the passage of time in years. The first was based on counting the number of years for which a named king or emperor had reigned.[16] The second depended on combining cycles of years of relatively short duration to establish longer cycles. The Chinese *kan-chih* system, based on a *kan* cycle of 10 characters and a *chih* cycle of 12 characters, has been used to count years for more than two millennia (and its use for counting days is even more ancient).

This means that the designation of year by two characters, one *kan* and the other *chih*, repeats itself every 60 years, but this allows for exact dating when combined with the name of an emperor (provided that he does not reign for more than 60 years which has happened only once in Chinese history, in the eighteenth century).

There is in fact no theoretical limit to the length of cycles, because every combination of two cycles establishes a new one, which in turn can be part of new combinations. Historically this process was carried furthest by the ancient Maya civilisations of Central America, which established the 'long count', which lasted 5126 years before repeating itself. Within the long count every single year can be defined by the points reached in the cycles comprising it, so that, for instance, the dates of successive solar eclipses are recorded as 12–5–9–7–2 10 Ik 15 Uo and 12–5–13–13–7 2 Manik 10 Mol,[17] which are equivalent to 17 September 1466 and 30 December 1470 – both dates recorded for Mexico in Theodor von Oppolzer's *Canon of Eclipses*. In both cases, note that the actual day is specified twice, in the first case as 10 Ik 15 Uo and in the second as 2 Manik 10 Mol. The first component, 10 Ik or 2 Manik, belongs to the so-called Tzolkin cycle of 260 days, every one of which is uniquely defined by a number from 1 to 20, and one of thirteen calendar signs, of which those for Ik and Manik are two. The same principle is adopted for the second component, but in this case there are eighteen calendar signs, so that a complete cycle has 360 days – which means that with the addition of five extra days it measures the length of the year. Both cycles operate on the same principle as the Chinese *kan-chih*.

All this may seem foreign to our own culture, but just think of referring to two dates in 1999 as Tuesday the 15th and Wednesday the 11th, and then having to work out not only which of them comes first, but also the number of days that separate them. The latter date can only be that of the

165

solar eclipse, 11 August, 1999, since in no other month in 1999 is the 11th day a Wednesday. The same logic locates Tuesday the 15th uniquely in June, but Tuesday the 16th could be in February, March or November (a source of confusion to be found neither in the Maya Tzolkin nor in the Chinese *kan-chih* calendar). At all events, having discovered that Tuesday the 15th is in June and Wednesday the 11th in August, we have no difficulty in working out that there are exactly 57 days between the two dates. (It is a paradox of the Western calendar that its only perfect cycle, that defined by the seven days of the week, has no clear astronomical basis. It is true that four weeks can be taken to correspond to four successive phases of the moon, but this correspondence is neither exact nor particularly significant.)

In the Mayan calendar, with the 260-day Tzolkin cycle used in conjunction with that of the calendar year, every day has a date in both cycles so that any combination of two such dates repeats itself only every 52 years,[18] a period of cosmic significance in pre-colonial Mexico. In relation to the 260-day Tzolkin cycle, the question is whether it has any astronomical basis. Anthony Aveni points out[19] that $2 \times 260 = 3 \times 173\frac{1}{3}$, and that $173\frac{1}{3}$ is a good approximation to the number of days between two successive lunar eclipses; this follows from the fact, already noted on page 96, that twice this number is almost equal to the number of days, 346.62, in an eclipse year. This explains why the Tzolkin cycle is far more useful than the annual cycle as an eclipse predictor.

It was certainly essential to the Maya, with their obsession with astrology, to fit astronomical events which recurred at regular intervals into the cycles of the calendar. The Maya were particularly interested in the synodic period of Venus, which is the time between successive instances of the planet appearing at a fixed point in the sky at the same time of day, for example due east at its first appearance after sunset. This period happens to be just short of 584 days, which means that five such periods add up to almost exactly eight years: this allows any observation of Venus to be repeated, with the same time and space coordinates, at intervals of exactly eight years. (Nothing, of course, is ever quite so convenient in astronomy, so that over the long term corrections will have to be made in the observations.) Even so, the fact that the 260-day Tzolkin cycle fits so neatly into the calendric system does suggest that eclipses, however irregular the occurrence in comparison to the periodicity of Venus, still had an important place in Mayan astrology.

When it comes to measuring and recording the passage of time in the course of a single day, two related problems must be solved. The first is to establish a standard for dividing up the time-span of a day into smaller units; the second is to find a reliable and accurate means of measuring the passage of time in such units. In solving these problems, astronomical phenomena are only marginally helpful: they certainly do not define, directly, any interval of time shorter than a day. None the less, the ancient Egyptians (who first used the gnomon in 1500 BC) divided 'the day – or rather the night – into fixed units of time, by choosing fixed stars, spaced at equal intervals across the sky, as reference points [and this] led to the development . . . of the prototype for the 24-hour day'.[20] It was not the Egyptians, however, but the Babylonians who were to establish standard units for the measurement of time, which continue to this day as the 60 minutes (each of 60 seconds) in one hour. The Babylonians also developed water-clocks, which were used for measuring the times of almost all their recorded eclipses, and the Chinese, quite independently, followed after about AD 400.

By the beginning of the telescopic era in astronomy, the West was already far ahead of the rest of the world, as the Jesuit missionary, Matteo Ricci, was able to prove to the Chinese when he visited their country at the end of the sixteenth century. By this time the civilisations of the ancient Middle East, with their cuneiform writing, had long passed into oblivion (except in the records of outsiders, such as the Old Testament stories of the Babylonian captivity of the Jews). The measurement of time was their one enduring legacy. The invention of the telescope coincided with vastly improved methods of timekeeping whose accuracy depended ultimately on a correct understanding of Newtonian gravitation. This brings us to our own day, in which Big Ben – a pendulum clock – though it still strikes the hours, does so by reference to time told by a caesium clock. *Sic transit gloria mundi*.

8

History, Sacred and Profane

Canon, calamity and ritual response

What makes possible a canon of eclipses, as enshrined in
Theodor von Oppolzer's monumental work of 1887, is
simply the fact that astronomy, corrected where necessary
by geophysics, has unlocked the door to a complete and
accurate record of eclipses, both solar and lunar, from the
beginning to the end of time. If you want to know about
the space and time coordinates for any eclipse that has
occurred in the past or will occur in the future, all you need
do today is put the right program in your computer. In this
respect there is nothing that sets eclipses apart from any
number of other astronomical phenomena, such as planetary
conjunctions, which have been observed from ancient times.
The only problem is that this hardly adds up to history,
unless, of course, the human dimension counts for nothing
– which would make a nonsense of history in any normal
sense of the word.

The history of eclipses is essentially the story of how
humankind has reacted to them. The problem facing the

169

historian – dealing with what is essentially a sporadic event – is to find what principles determined the way people reacted in any particular case. What is more, the historian will know that all such principles are, in the end, redundant since eclipses have no lasting material effects, requiring human intervention to restore the *status quo ante*.

The historical record, even up to the present day, shows that when it comes to eclipses, practice is far from principle. From the earliest days of humankind the response to a solar eclipse, unless it was a simple, spontaneous outburst of emotion, was always intended to counteract it in one way or another. The popular belief was that if no action was taken the eclipse would have some malign effect (although occasionally eclipses were seen as auspicious). Once eclipses began to be recorded, in both the Old World and the New, those who kept the records came to belong to some high-status priestly caste, whose advice was often sought by those in power. In particular, they were expected to be able to predict eclipses so that countermeasures could be taken in advance of the event.

Lessons from the Bible

Power over the Sun – as the priestly record-keepers claimed for themselves – is a form of supernatural power, familiar in the Western world from the biblical record. Although the Bible contains no more than oblique references to solar eclipses, the fundamental principle, in both the Old and the New Testament, is not only that God can interfere with the course of the Sun, but also that he may actually do so (although, as we shall see later, God is often seen as preferring to hold his hand). As God said to Amos, a great prophet of doom, 'on that day ... I will make the Sun go down at noon, and darken the Earth in broad daylight,'[1] which is a

170

good description of totality in a solar eclipse. The question, to be considered shortly, is whether God ever carried out his threat.

When it comes to the Sun, the Old Testament record goes back to the story of the creation in Chapter I of the Book of Genesis. What this has to say about the Sun played a key part in the debate between creationism and evolution that was central to the famous Scopes trial, held in the state of Tennessee in 1925. By a recent enactment, the state had made it

unlawful for any teacher in any of the . . . public schools of the state . . . to teach any theory that denies the story of the divine creation of man as taught in the Bible, and to teach instead that man has descended from any lower order of animals.[2]

The accused, John Scopes, was a high-school teacher who had deliberately defied this law in order to provoke a trial. He succeeded beyond his wildest dreams.

The law was the result of campaigning by William Jennings Bryan, who not only led the fundamentalist movement in the United States but was also one of the country's best-known citizens (who had three times stood for President). Bryan had offered to give evidence for the prosecution in the trial. Scopes, however, was defended by Clarence Darrow – probably the best-known defence attorney in American legal history. In the courtroom the judge and the accused remained on the sidelines. The trial became a debate between Bryan and Darrow, focused largely upon what the Old Testament taught about God and the Sun – particularly, though by no means exclusively, in relation to the creation of the world.

At a key moment in the trial, Darrow, having asked Bryan whether he believed that God had made the Sun on the fourth day of creation, went on to read from the biblical narrative:

> And God said, let there be lights in the firmament of heaven to divide the day from the night; and let them be for signs, and for seasons, and for days, and years. And let them be for lights in the firmament of heaven to give light upon the earth: and it was so. And God made two great lights; the greater light to rule the day, and the lesser light to rule the night; He made the stars also. And God set them in the firmament of the heaven to give light upon the earth, and to rule over the day and over the night, and to divide the light from the darkness: and God saw that it was good. And the evening and the morning were the fourth day.[3]

The Bible, always economical with words, tells a great deal in this short passage. In fact it almost told too much to hold its ground against Darrow, who challenged Bryan to explain how, without the Sun, night could be told from day during the first *three* days of creation. For our present purposes we do not need to know how Bryan met this challenge: what is important is that, by divine ordinance, the Sun rules the day and the Moon rules the night. By necessary implication, any departure from this scheme requires divine intervention, as the prophet Amos certainly believed. It would seem, then, that there is no room for solar eclipses in the biblical ordering of the cosmos.

Joshua, who after the death of Moses led the Israelites across the River Jordan and into the promised land, not surprisingly found that the new settlers, under his command, were not entirely welcomed by the Amorites and other people who already lived there. No matter: God was on their side, and ready to intervene in a way which today would be called pro-active. God delivered the Amorites, led by their five kings, into the hands of Israel. Joshua, wishing to confirm his victory, cried out:

'Sun, stand thou still at Gibeon, and thou moon in the valley of Ajalon'. And the sun stood still, and the moon stayed until the nations took vengeance on their enemies . . . There has been no day like it before or since when the LORD hearkened to the voice of a man; for the LORD fought for Israel.[4]

The day the Sun stood still is one of the best known of all incidents recounted in the Bible. The phenomenon, whatever it was, is difficult to interpret as a solar eclipse, but the implicit message is clear enough: only God intervenes with the Sun in its course. The prophet Amos testified thus when predicting an event which, from his description, could certainly be a solar eclipse. Another prophet, Joel, went even further, and saw the same phenomenon as one of the 'portents' that God would give 'in the heavens and on the earth . . . before [the coming of HIS] great and terrible day'.[5]

The day the Sun stood still, as reported in the book of Joshua, took up some time in the debate between Darrow and Bryan during the Scopes trial, and neither side moved an inch. Bryan simply accepted the fundamental truth of the Bible – God's word could not be taken in vain. The strain was too much for him; he died five days after the end of the trial. A quarter of a century later, Immanuel Velikovsky, an American psychiatrist, took a different tack when he claimed in his book *Worlds in Collision* that Joshua, Chapter 10 – as quoted above – was historical. Velikovsky also went much further than this, conceiving of a whole celestial scenario in which not only the Earth and the Moon, but comets and planets too, all interacted in a way which defied every serious astronomer from Hipparchus onwards. Astronomers, asked for their reactions to Velikovsky, had any number of ways of demonstrating that his ideas were absurd, and these are beautifully deployed in E. C. Krupp's short study 'When worlds collide: The Velikovsky catastrophe'.[6] The more the astronomers protested, the faster people bought Velikovsky's book – but it is now almost completely forgotten.

The theological implications of Velikovsky are significant. In the Tennessee courtroom, Bryan wisely adopted the principle stated by the American writer Elbert Hubbard: 'Never explain – your friends do not need it and your enemies will not believe you anyway.'[7] Velikovsky ignored this advice, and conceived of a God who constantly disturbed the established motion of the planets and other heavenly bodies in order to set in train a series of disparate events outside the observed order of the cosmos – of which the Sun standing still is only one – recorded in the Old Testament. This sort of unprogrammed pro-active intervention would be ideal for explaining events like solar eclipses, but the question then arises as to why God, having established a beautifully ordered Universe (a theme central in the thinking of Aristotle and Thomas Aquinas) would ever choose to disturb it. At the end of the day, the real truth of the matter is the opposite of that put forward by Velikovsky: God is not pro-active. The Book of Isaiah gets it right when the prophet says, 'Truly thou art a God who hidest thyself,'[8] and the whole subsequent history of the Jewish people bears this out.

This point comes up again, at its most controversial, in the New Testament. In the Good Friday narrative, the first three gospels, Matthew, Mark and Luke (almost certainly using a common source), in recounting the three hours spent by Jesus on the cross, tell how, from 'about the sixth hour . . . there was darkness over the whole land until the ninth hour, while the sun's light failed.'[9] If this is to be explained historically (and without the sort of fantasy resorted to by Velikovsky), then a solar eclipse is the only possible event that would explain how 'the sun's light failed'.

There are a number of objections to this conclusion, none of which can easily be overcome. First no solar eclipse recorded in the *Canon of Eclipses* is consistent with the time and place of the biblical narrative: no solar eclipse took place close to Jerusalem in any year which fits the chronology now established by scholars. Second, the crucifixion is recorded as having taken place in the season of the Jewish passover, which always coincides with the full Moon; solar eclipses occur at new Moon. Third, three hours' darkness far exceeds the possible time limits of totality in any solar eclipse, whatever allowances are made. (However, two medieval eclipses – on 3 June 1239, as observed from Coimbra in Portugal, and on 6 October 1241, as observed from Reichersberg in Germany – are recorded as having lasted three and four hours, respectively: far longer than is actually possible. In an era without accurate timepieces, when most records were kept by religious houses, it is understandable how the time between first and fourth contact came to be equated with the period of darkness at the time of the crucifixion.)

According to modern scholarship, the first three gospels are not eyewitness accounts of the events recorded. The original author of the passage quoted above heard the account at second if not third hand. In retelling the story it was critically important, in the religious climate of first-century Palestine, to establish that what had taken place was the fulfilment of a prophecy. This is frequently emphasized in the gospel narratives, and the words 'that the prophecy might be fulfilled' continually appear. Darkness at noon, as prophesied by Joel and Amos, would confirm the claim of the gospel-writers that Jesus was the Messiah.

Going back to these two Old Testament prophets, the question is whether their prophecy related to an actual personal experience or was based on no more than a folk memory. Scholars date the Book of Amos to the eighth century BC, and it could well be that its author either witnessed the solar eclipse of 15 June 763 BC or at least heard accurate reports of it. The path of totality certainly crossed Assyria – the source of the only known record of this eclipse – but the prophet himself is unlikely to have been present at any locality on the path. Even so, he could well have heard accurate reports of the phenomenon of totality. This is even more likely in the case of Joel (whose prophecy dates from the fourth century BC), who could have witnessed, in Palestine, any one of three possible total eclipses.[10]

When it comes to the New Testament, scholars recognise the possibility that Luke, in adding the words 'while the sun's light failed' to the passion narrative, was relating it to his own experience, as a young man living in the neighbourhood of Antioch in Syria, of the total eclipse of 24 November AD 29. On the other hand, the use of the Greek word *ekleipein* (from which our 'eclipse' derives), meaning 'fail', in the context of the Sun does not necessarily imply a solar eclipse.[11] When comparing the Old and New Testaments, there is therefore an important distinction to be drawn: the prophets were predicting events in the indefinite future, whereas the gospel-writers purported to relate events of the recent past. In terms of historical truth, there is a world of difference between the two.

For the modern historian of solar eclipses, the study of the Bible leads to only one conclusion: the place of the Sun, whether in the story of the creation or in the narratives recounting the fortunes and tribulations of the people of Israel, provides no material of any kind that is even remotely useful. The definitive study, Stephenson's *Historical Eclipses and Earth's Rotation*, makes no use whatever of biblical sources. From the perspective of what it has to say about solar eclipses, the hard record of history, covering a period of nearly three millennia, supports the agnostic Clarence Darrow against the Christian fundamentalist William Jennings Bryan. But this is not quite the end of the story. The

Old Testament does provide us with a possible interface between the Jewish religious tradition and the astronomical records of Babylon. We have already met Nebuchadnezzar as king of a country obsessed with recording astronomical phenomena, eclipses included. But one question has so far been left unanswered: quite simply, just why was this so important?

If the tens of thousands of cuneiform records (most of which are now in the British Museum) provide no answer to this question, the first six chapters of the Book of Daniel, in the Old Testament, at least suggest one. When Nebuchadnezzar was king, he held the people of Israel captive in Babylon – a historical trauma they have never forgotten. The portrait of the king painted in the Book of Daniel is of a man obsessed with power, and terrified by what fate might hold in store for him. His son, Belshazzar, who succeeded him, was no different. Both father and son had continually to come to terms with ominous events, on one occasion a dream, on another a hand writing mysteriously on the wall at the climax of a great feast.

The first reaction of the terrified king to any such event was to consult the court astrologers. Significantly, in the whole of the Bible the Hebrew word for astrologer, *ashshaph*, occurs only in the Book of Daniel, where it always refers to the astrologers at the court of the King of Babylon. These astrologers we can regard as representatives of the countless stargazers who over the centuries had recorded the celestial phenomena – including eclipses – recorded on all those clay tablets in the British Museum. The Book of Daniel provides our only evidence that they ever failed in their task of interpreting untoward events as portents in the lives of the kings whose courts they served. It also suggests that death was the penalty for such failure.[12]

Significantly, the two great stories of the Book of Daniel – of Nebuchadnezzar's dream of the great image with feet of clay, and the writing on the wall during Belshazzar's feast – have nothing to do with celestial phenomena. Strictly speaking, then, they were outside the competence of the professional astrologers who failed to interpret them. In the end both kings, father and son, in their desperation consulted Daniel, a Jewish youth whom Nebuchadnezzar had commanded to serve in his palace. Daniel, asked to explain the king's dream, made clear that 'no wise men, enchanters, magicians or astrologers [could] show the king the mystery which the king had asked' and went on to declare that 'there [was] a God in heaven who reveal[ed] mysteries'.[13] The Jewish God revealed to Daniel not only the contents of the king's dream, but also its doom-laden interpretation, which could have provided Nebuchadnezzar with little comfort.

The story of Belshazzar's feast shows Daniel interpreting the writing on the wall in a way which could have accorded with the rules of astrology, had the court astrologers dared to apply them. The words were MENE, MENE, TEKEL and PARSIN. MENE meant 'God has numbered the days of your kingdom and brought it to an end; TEKEL, you have been weighed in the balances and been found wanting; PARSIN, your kingdom is divided and given to the Medes and Persians.'[14] Only too true: Belshazzar was slain the very same night, and Darius, the Mede, inherited the kingdom.

The Bible provides a footnote on the fall of Babylon. The great prophet of the Jewish exile, known to biblical scholars as the *second* Isaiah (who according to the biblical record would have been a contemporary of Daniel), in proclaiming God's judgement on Babylon, challenged the astrologers: 'Let them stand forth and save you, those who divide the heavens, who gaze at the stars, who at the new moons predict what shall befall you.'[15] The reference to 'new moons' suggests, obliquely, astrologers' interpretations appropriate to a solar eclipse, which can occur only at the time of a new Moon.

What, then, does the cuneiform record (which tells us nothing about Daniel or the second Isaiah) have to say about such interpretations? This record is quite overwhelming, but in spite of all the astrologers ranged against Daniel it contains little information about how they interpreted eclipses at any stage in the history of Babylon. This is astonishing, since what other reason could there have been for all their meticulous observations? It may be that the records of time and place were essential for predicting future eclipses, whereas the interpretation of any single eclipse was a one-off taking into account political factors so well-known at the time that there was no need to record them. More than likely, it was prudent not to do so.

Oddly enough, the few Assyrian records, although from earlier times, tell us more about the interpretation of eclipses. The chronicles for the year 763 BC record insurrection in the city of Assur in the same month as the Sun was eclipsed. The record of the solar eclipse of 27 May 669 BC goes further: 'If the Sun is rising like a crescent and wears a crown like the Moon: the king will capture the enemy's land; evil will leave the land, and [the land] will experience good . . .'[16] The scribe, Rasil, was a Babylonian, but it is still remarkable that the records of the countless scribes who followed him after the kingdom of Babylon was established in the seventh century BC tell us so little about *interpreting* eclipses. It is time, therefore, to turn to other parts of the world.

The Chinese empire

The first country to look at is China, where, some time in the mythical past,

[the Emperor Yao] commanded the [brothers] Hsi and Ho, in reverent accordance with the august heavens, to

179

compute and delineate the sun, moon and stars, and the celestial markers, and so to deliver respectfully the seasons to be observed by the people.[17]

The two brothers were responsible for preventing eclipses, and the story told is that when they failed to predict a solar eclipse the emperor had them beheaded. Joseph Needham describes the age from which the story originates as 'what might be called a period legendary in character', and notes that if the fateful eclipse ever did occur, it could have been as early as 2165 BC or as late as 1948 BC.[18]

The earliest authenticated eclipse recorded (on an oracle bone) by the Chinese occurred in 1217 BC. By this time the tradition that an eclipse, whether of the Sun or the Moon, was the result of some heavenly dragon satisfying its hunger was already established. The tradition spread throughout the Far East, and continues to this day.[19] In fact, the Chinese had a good grasp of the astronomy of eclipses more than two thousand years ago. Liu Hsiang's *Wu Ching Thung I* (The Fundamental Ideas of the Five Classics) stated the true position: 'When the sun is eclipsed it is because the moon hides him as she moves on her way.'[20] By this time the solar eclipses of 442, 382, 300 and 96 BC had all been recorded, and by the third century AD the Chinese astronomers could predict eclipses with remarkable accuracy. This meant a radical change in their interpretation: once eclipses could be predicted they became, in a sense, tamed, and were no longer regarded as 'reprimands from heaven'.[21] In comparison with the Western world, the Chinese may have noted the solar corona at a very early stage – perhaps as early as the second millennium BC.

According to one possible meaning, recognised by scholars, characters on an oracle bone fragment – from not later than the solar eclipse of 1281 BC – could describe how 'three flames ate up the sun, and a great star was visible'.

This could be a record of 'coronal streamers, or possibly of especially striking solar prominences (flame-like masses of gas which sometime appear at the sun's limb)'.[22]

The expectation that ominous consequences will follow from eclipses goes back a long way in Chinese history. A text from the second millennium BC records how the king interpreted an oracle based on a solar eclipse with the words 'There will be disaster but it will not rain.'[23] Some thousand years later, in the time of the Chou dynasty, reports take an almost standard form: 'The Sun was eclipsed; drums were beaten and oxen were sacrificed at the Temple.' This is probably the first mention anywhere of a ritual response to a solar eclipse. We shall see later how, in many different parts of the world, solar eclipses have provoked similar reactions – even up to the present day.

The association of solar eclipses with calamity continued even after they could be more or less accurately predicted. An astrological treatise, commenting on the solar eclipse of 28 August AD 360, notes how

> Whenever an eclipse covers a small portion of the Sun the calamity it brings will be relatively small, but when it covers a large portion of the Sun the consequences will be much more serious.[24]

On this particular occasion the Emperor Mu died less than a year later, aged only nineteen. Twice in previous centuries, following the eclipses of 4 March 181 BC and 18 January AD 121, a similar fate had befallen the dowager empress.[25] Given a record of this kind it is hardly surprising that the astrologers were always close to the imperial court, as they were to remain until the end of the last dynastic empire at the beginning of the twentieth century.

In its understanding of eclipses and reactions to them, Japan followed China. In both countries offices were closed on the day of a solar eclipse. During the turbulent years of medieval Japan the accurate prediction of eclipses was particularly important, and the court astrologers were tempted to over-predict. If a predicted eclipse failed to occur there was no question of their losing face – on the contrary, they were rewarded for their success in preventing it. They, in turn, gave all the credit to the emperor, congratulating him on his virtue, which was clearly what had prevented the eclipse.[26]

The Western world: ancient and medieval

In Europe, a well-known interpretation of a solar eclipse is to be found in an ode by Pindar, a Greek poet who was probably writing about the total solar eclipse that could be observed from Thebes on 30 April 463 BC:

> Beam of the sun! O thou that seest from afar, what will thou be devising? O mother of mine eyes! O star supreme reft from us in the daytime! Why hast thou perplexed the power of man and the way of wisdom, by rushing forth on a darksome track? Art thou bringing us some new and strange disaster? Yet by Zeus, I implore thee thou swift driver of steeds. Do thou, O queen! Change this world-wide portent into some painless blessing for Thebes . . .
>
> But art thou bringing a sign of some war, or wasting of produce, or an unspeakably violent snow-storm, or fatal faction, or again, some overflowing of the sea on the plain, or frost to bind the earth, or heat of the south wind streaming with raging rain? Or wilt thou, by deluging the land, cause the race of men to begin anew?[27]

This says it all: Pindar's ode embraces every type of calamity, natural or political. His appeal to change the por-

tent into a blessing for Thebes (from where he himself probably witnessed the eclipse) is particularly poignant. The
record does not tell us, however, of any specific calamities
for which the eclipse could be seen as a portent.

The tradition of solar eclipse as portent continued for at
least another thousand years. At the end of the fifth century
AD, Marinus Neapolitanus, head of the Athenian School
of Philosophy, wrote about the death of one of its most
distinguished members, the philosopher Proclus:

> A year before his death there were various omens. There
> was an eclipse of the sun which was so pronounced as to
> turn day into night and the darkness was deep enough for
> the stars to become visible . . . They say that such events
> as are observed to happen in the heavens are indicative of
> things that happen on earth; so that these eclipses clearly
> foretold us of the privation and departure as it were of
> the light of philosophy.[28]

The way Marinus links an event observed in the heavens
(most probably the solar eclipse of 14 January AD 484) with
things that happen on earth is particularly apt for the only
occasion when the shadow of a heavenly body is cast onto
the surface of the Earth. Significantly, he suggests no ritual
means that might have prevented the death of Proclus. Such
a measure, however, is reported by the Roman historian,
Livy, for a much earlier eclipse – probably that which was
total in Rome on 17 July 188 BC:

> Before the new magistrates departed for their provinces,
> a three-day period of prayer was proclaimed in the name
> of the College of Decemvirs at all the street corner shrines
> because in the daytime, between about the third and
> fourth hours, darkness had covered everything.[29]

Prayer as a reaction to a solar eclipse has continued to the present day, particularly in the Christian world. This, then, is our next focus of attention. Stephenson provides detailed descriptions of some nineteen solar eclipses, observed from sixty-two locations ranging from Iceland to Syria, in the period from 840 to 1605. By this latter date the medieval world had long given way to the modern, and the sixteenth-century records are, for the most part, strictly matter of fact. The Table below lists sixteen of Stephenson's eclipses, observed from twenty-one locations, in the period before 1500. The records of these eclipses I shall analyse according to a number of different themes.

Table 2 Some total eclipses recorded in the West, 800–1500.

Date of eclipse	Observed from
5 May 840	Bergamo (Italy)
11 August 1124	Novgorod (Russia)
2 August 1133	Kerkrade (Holland)
20 March 1140	Malmesbury (England)
11 April 1176	Antioch (Syria)
1 May 1185	Novgorod
14 May 1230	Belvoir (England)
3 June 1239	Coimbra (Portugal), Arezzo, Florence, Siena (Italy), Split (Croatia)
6 October 1241	Split (Croatia)
25 May 1267	Constantinople (Eastern Roman Empire)
5 July 1312	Eastern Iceland
16 June 1406	Hamburg and Magdeburg (Germany)
7 June 1415	Prague (Bohemia), Wrocław (Poland), Kobrin (Belarus)
12 February 1431	Perugia (Italy)
25 February 1476	Pskov (Russia)
16 March 1485	Augsburg (Germany)

The most common popular reaction was distress and terror (840, 1124, 1133, 1415), often coupled with fear that the world was coming to an end (840, 1133, 1239, 1406). Kerkrade reported for 1133 how 'the face of the world was sad, terrible, black, wonderful'.[30] Seven years later, Malmesbury reported how 'men seated at tables, as almost everywhere they were at that time, for it was Lent, feared the primeval chaos'. At Arezzo (1239), 'all the animals and birds were terrified; and the wild beasts could easily be caught'. The 1239 eclipse produced a number of valuable records – mostly from monasteries – since the path of totality passed across many major centres of learning of the day. Sometimes, as in Florence, the reaction was more muted, and we are told no more than 'that many people ignorant of the course of the Sun and the other planets marvelled greatly' – a statement suggesting that the reporter, almost certainly a monk, knew better. When the region of totality left Italy, crossing the Adriatic Sea to Croatia, the reaction, as reported from Split was much more pronounced: 'such great fear overtook everyone, that just like madmen they ran about too and fro shrieking, thinking that the end of the world had come'. Split in fact experienced a double whammy, because it also lay on the path of totality of the 1141 eclipse, which produced 'great terror among everyone, just as in that eclipse, which happened three years previously'.

Needless to say, the religious dimension often dominated popular reactions. In Novgorod (1185) it was reported how 'it was terrible to see this sign of the Lord', and from Coimbra (1239) we learn how 'there occurred a sign such as never happened since the Passion of our Lord until the present day . . . Many people assembled in the church of the Holy Cross.'

The reactions of birds and animals are also noted, as in a report from Antioch of a 'sad and terrifying sight, which caused many people to lament with weeping; the sheep, oxen and horses crowded together in terror'. Moving on to a different time, and a quite different location, we learn from Kobrin, in Belarus, how 'King Vladislav and his followers were at first astonished and bewildered, later full of reverence [at the eclipse of 1415]. For it was so notable that the birds, terrified by the sudden darkness, fell to the ground . . .' Later in the century, a report from Augsburg (1485) related how 'crazed birds fell from the sky and bleating flocks and fearful herds of oxen unexpectedly began to return from their pastures to their stables'.

Few reports noted how order is immediately restored after the end of the eclipse. An exception is an account from Pskov (1476), which noted that 'people could not see one another on the market nor anywhere else in the town and they were very frightened; and again God gave us light as before'. Some reports were remarkably matter-of-fact: of the phlegmatic Englishmen of Belvoir, in 1230, it is reported how 'workers in the fields and many others, leaving their morning's work on account of the excessive darkness, decided to return to bed and go back to sleep', while nine years later, in Siena, 'people lit lamps in houses and shops'. A 1415 report from Prague struck a religious tone relating how 'Mass could not be celebrated without lights'.

Given the biblical tradition of regarding signs in the heavens as portents, remarkably few of the solar eclipses witnessed by medieval Christendom seem to have been interpreted in this way. The 1267 eclipse at Constantinople was seen by some as a portent of 'the very great and destructive calamities which were soon to be vented on the Romans by the Turks', and at the other end of Christendom, the eclipse over Eastern Iceland in 1312 was followed by 'a great mortality of men'.

In all the instances related above, it is significant (at least to me as an anthropologist) how little was done to bring an eclipse to an end. The reaction of medieval Christendom, however great the sense of doom, was essentially passive. The hand of God was seen behind every eclipse, but people seemed to know that their fate depended on submitting to His will, so that churches became crowded, with candles lit in the gloom, while the birds and animals outside reacted, according to their kind, to the fall of darkness.

Science and traditional belief in the modern world

The religious dimension of eclipses was itself not entirely eclipsed in the modern Western world. The *Dorset County Observer* of 9 September 1847 noted, with respect to the solar eclipse that would occur exactly a month later, that

it seems generally to be admitted by thoughtful persons that phenomena connected with astronomical sciences are of all others the best calculated to impress the mind with exalted thoughts of the greatness of divine power. Although it would be wrong to deprecate others of God's works ... there is no doubt something in the vastness of that which is beyond and above us which calls us more readily away from what is within and around and beneath us, to the contemplation of him who made all things. There is another, it may be, and lesser effect, and less often thought of, but it has both poetry and religion on its side, which is peculiarly applicable to the contemplation of astronomical phenomena. It is the bringing together of distant minds; the thought, to how many thousands of persons the same revelation of divine order, and arrangement, is exhibited, in some cases at the same moment, in others, as in that which is the subject of our present article, at successive moments or hours. So that it requires no very fanciful imagination, but only a very thoughtful watching of the hours as they pass to bring before our minds those persons from whom to us, or to whom from us, the phenomenon is passing one by one; and in more serious subjects such thoughts would give zest to the Missionary prayer of an English Christian offered in an evening hour, while the labourers in far distant lands for whom he prays are awaking to their day of Christian toil.

The genius of the unknown editor in combining the philosophy of Aristotle and Aquinas with the missionary zeal of imperial Britain, is almost too good to be true. The Scots, or at least the editors of the *Aberdeen Observer*, in reporting their eclipse of 15 May 1836, had played down the Christian aspect, describing the crowds gathered to view the eclipse as turning their faces 'towards the sun like Persian worshippers', while noting how at the same time 'in almost all the churches of this city, the hours of divine worship in the afternoon were very properly changed, for the desire to witness one of the most sublime phenomena of nature could with no good reason be regarded in the light of common curiosity'.

The first eclipse of the present century was on 28 May 1900, and the path of totality crossed Portugal, where a small group of British astronomers observed it. Their report noted how

> upon the lower classes of the community there fell a great dread, and in Estareja a number of peasant women sought the refuge of the church as totality drew on, and gave vent to their fears in prayers on their knees ... In Portugal there are only 20 per cent of the population who can read, and we are not surprised to find that among many of them the eclipse was associated with the end of the world.[31]

Some 14 years later the possible reactions of the common people of England were the subject of a long letter to the Astronomer Royal, marked 'PRIVATE and CONFIDEN-

TIAL', from Canon H. Bickersteth Ottley, the Secretary of the Imperial Sunday Alliance. The letter is dated 12 August 1914, a week after the outbreak of the First World War. It was a time of doom, and the subject of the letter was the invitation to a day of prayer, on Friday 21 August by 'the Leaders of the three main divisions of the Religious life of the Nation'. These dignitaries (representing only Christian churches) had failed to take into account 'A Total ECLIPSE of the SUN – partly visible at Greenwich'. This failure moved the Canon to a veritable flood of words:

> For reasons which, to all who know the superstitious minds of the vast proportion of the more ignorant and excitable populations of this (and other) countries, will be obvious enough, – more especially having regard to the terrible tension and anxiety prevalent among all classes with reference to the impending eventualities of this truly 'cataclysmic' and almost world-wide WAR, – it is felt, by all those to whom I have spoken on the subject, that it is for every reason most important that the Newspaper PRESS should be especially urged to give adequate pro-minence BEFOREHAND to the astronomical FACTS connected with the occurrence of ECLIPSES in general; and that every effort should be made to 'educate' the Masses of this and other Nations on the true nature of a Phenomenon which is, of course, merely one example of the magnificent LAW and ORDER of the Natural Universe; but which, unhappily, has – in past times – often given rise to scenes of hysterical and superstitious Terror and Panic, even, (as I believe) to the extent of causing Madness and Disease in the case of the feebler-minded and more delicate or ignorant members of rural or urban communities.

The canon went on to tell how the 'eminent Divines' had 'no desire or present intention of suggesting any alteration of the Date', suggesting rather that the popular press – encouraged by the Astronomer Royal – might help in

> PREVENTING any such public 'panic' as might well seize the imagination and nerves of not a few poor simple people if – possibly under the stimulus of some fanatical Religionists . . . leading to results disastrous to a true Faith and Trust in the Great CREATOR who wisely 'orders all things in Heaven and Earth'; and Who, while holding in His Hand the destinies of Nations, yet has appointed for the Stars of Heaven their majestic Laws . . .

The Canon accepted that it was outside 'the "official" province of the Astronomer Royal to take cognisance of popular "superstition"'. He was only too right. The Astronomer Royal was actually in Australia at the time. His chief assistant, replying from Greenwich, showed that the situation there was less fraught than at Westminster, and suggested – in the face of the 'eminent Divines' – that 'if the Day of National Prayer could be altered, this would probably be the best solution of the difficulty'. The canon's fears proved to be ill-founded. The eclipse was, in any case, only partial in England, and gave rise to no 'public panic'. The path of totality crossed European Russia from north to south, and – with the benefit of hindsight – the eminent divines of the Orthodox Church would have had every reason to see it as a portent for the terror that would overcome their country before the end of the war. I have not, however, found any report of how the common people of Russia reacted to the eclipse.

Even in the last decade of the twentieth century, popular reactions to a solar eclipse can be as unrestrained as ever they were in medieval Europe. For the eclipse of 11 July 1991 the Royal Observatory of Belgium sent a party to Lower California (actually part of Mexico) to a location where conditions for observation were expected to be optimal (which they proved to be). The operation was set up in the garden of the hotel where the astronomers were staying. During the few minutes of totality, which required intense concentration, they were disturbed by the weeping and wailing of the hotel staff, who were terrified by the unexpected fall of darkness. Certain acoustic signals were missed as a result, but the other observations and recordings were unimpaired.

At the solar eclipse of 24 October 1995, the reactions of the local population of the village of Jajai in India were recorded for British television's Channel 4.[32] The basic premise, popularly accepted by a village in the centre of the path of totality, was that the eclipse was potentially harmful, and required countermeasures on their part. The steps needed to be taken were orchestrated (almost literally) by the village holy man, who ordered loud music to be played as the sky darkened. At the same time people were enjoined to stay indoors, and pregnant women had to be smeared with a mixture of red sand and water which, according to tradition, had the power to prevent the birth of a defective child. This being India, cows received the same treatment, and children – with their schools closed – either went to the local temples or remained at home to drink large quantities of milk.

Changing the course of history

For all the countless occasions in the historical record of an eclipse being followed by calamity, whether it be the death of the ruler, plague or famine, or some natural disaster, there are few of which it can be said that changed the course of history. We have already noted the eclipse that is always cited as having had a decisive historical effect. This was the one that took place during battle between the Medes and Lydians (which according to eclipse astronomy could only have taken place on 28 May 585 BC) and caused fighting to cease. Here, both Herodotus' history and the recorded prediction of the eclipse by Thales are open to doubt. None the less, if the incident did actually happen then it is probably the most important of its kind in the whole of world history. A comparable incident, relating to the eclipse of 15 August 310 BC, was reported by Diodorus Siculus, a Roman historian of the first century BC. In the course of a war with Carthage, the tyrant Agathocles escaped with his fleet from the harbour at Syracuse, which was blockaded by Carthage; the fleet was pursued by the Carthaginians, but was rescued by nightfall. His good fortune turned upon him the next day with the occurrence of a solar eclipse, which, interpreted by his sailors as a portent of misfortune, created great anxiety among them.[33]

Outside the ancient world, the only instance of an eclipse having influenced the course of war is recorded in Japan, for the year 1183. At this time the Japanese were fighting their equivalent of the English Wars of the Roses. Two of the strongest clans, the Minamoto and the Taira, were fighting for control of the country. Just as the Minamoto camp was preparing for battle with the Taira, their soldiers fled, frightened by a solar eclipse – a phenomenon for which they had no rational explanation.[34]

Some 461 years after the Minamoto flight from battle, Adam Schall, a Jesuit missionary in China, was to use the occasion of an eclipse to transform the astronomy of the imperial court. In the summer of 1644 he challenged the court astrologers to predict the timing of the eclipse due to occur on 1 September. They accepted his challenge, but when the day came Schall's predictions proved to be more accurate. As a result he was asked to take over the office of court astrologer. In this capacity, according to a critical Dominican,

Father Adam, being president of the College of Mathematics, had the charge of, as well in Political and in

192

Religious respects, assigning lucky and unlucky days for everything they are to do [choosing] days and hours for everything except eating, drinking and sinning.[35]

Court intrigue cost Adam Schall his office, but in 1669 another Jesuit, Ferdinand Verbiest, once again successfully challenged the traditional Chinese astrologers. By this time the imperial court had learnt the lesson: Jesuit astronomy was superior to their home-grown version. It was only the suppression of the Jesuit Order by Pope Clement XIV in 1773 that put an end to the regime of Jesuits as astrologers to the Emperor of China.

That an eclipse could be as significant in the history of the New World as in the Old is shown by the story of Tenskwatawa, the Shawnee prophet (Figure 8.1). In the

Figure 8.1 The Shawnee prophet Tenskwatawa.

early years of the nineteenth century, Thomas Jefferson, third President of the United States, was committed to a policy of settling the vast territories west of the Appalachian mountains. This required the pacification of the territories of Ohio and Indiana, where the Shawnee tribe, with its great leader Tecumseh, was dominant. In 1805 Tecumseh's twin brother, Tenskwatawa, appeared as a prophet, declaring that 'he had been taken up into the spirit world and had been permitted to lift the veil of the past and the future'.

The new prophet attracted considerable support, but he risked losing it by overplaying his hand, 'dreaming dreams and announcing wonderful revelations from time to time. A miracle which finally silenced all objections was the prediction of an eclipse of the sun which took place in the summer of 1806; this was followed by his enthusiastic acceptance as a true prophet and messenger of the Master of Life.' New prophecies came thick and fast, including one of a 'great catastrophe, [to] take place within four years, which only the adherents of the new prophet would escape'. In 1811 the Shawnee uprising, inspired by Tenskwatawa and led by Tecumseh, was finally put down by William Henry Harrison, Governor of Indiana Territory, at the battle of Tippecanoe, but the 'religious fervor that [Tenskwatawa] created among the Indian tribes [was] equalled at no time since the beginning of white contact'.[36] This is saying a great deal, for the native Americans, until their final defeat in 1890 at the battle of Wounded Knee, were continually led by charismatic figures such as Tenskwatawa. The solar eclipse of 1806 helped make him one of the greatest.

Eclipse demography

Besides looking at the way people have reacted to eclipses over the course of history, it is interesting to calculate just

194

how many – in the tens of thousands of years of *Homo sapiens sapiens* – have actually experienced a total solar eclipse. This is the task of eclipse demography, which, so far as I can tell, is an entirely new field. This leaves me free to define its subject matter. The starting point is simply the number of people who can be reckoned to have experienced any one instance of a total solar eclipse (including those whom poor weather deprived of the complete experience described in Chapter 1). At the same time, given the vast number – some tens of thousands – of solar eclipses experienced by people in one part of the world or another, some means must be found of making the subject manageable. In practice, the complete absence of useful records for any but the last three thousand years goes a long way towards solving this particular problem. In this period some two thousand total solar eclipses have occurred. During all the tens of thousands of years preceding it, the world's population was much too small and scattered to be significant for eclipse demography.

It would still be a gigantic task to relate the recorded eclipses for the last three thousand years, listed in order of time, to the number of people who may be counted as having observed them. This, however, is quite unnecessary. The number of eclipses to take into consideration can be drastically reduced by including only those that can be reckoned to have been seen by more than a specified number of people. Even if a low number is specified, this immediately eliminates the great majority of eclipses, simply because the path of totality crossed either the sea or very sparsely populated areas of land (as was the case with the South Atlantic eclipse of 30 June 1992 or the Siberian eclipse of 9 March 1997). On this basis about half the twentieth-century eclipses would drop out of the reckoning. But the procedure can be simplified still more drastically.

Before doing so, I shall turn from the record of eclipses (which with the help of modern science can be extended

195

back into the indefinite past) to a quite different subject, historical demography – a recent technique for studying population movements in the past. Inevitably it includes the study of population growth. To get the perspective right, before the agricultural revolution, which began some ten thousand years ago, the population of the world never reached ten million – even though by this time both the Old and New Worlds were inhabited. The distribution of this small population was determined by the local resources offered by the land to hunter-gatherers, and along the coast to fishermen. Needless to say, it was quite different to the distribution at any stage of recorded history. Quite simply, the agricultural revolution, and all the developments that followed in its wake, made possible the growth of the world's population to the point reached today, where the accepted figure is between five and six billion.

This vast increase is, above all, a phenomenon of the twentieth century. It is estimated that at the beginning of the Christian era, two thousand years ago, the human population was approximately a third of a billion – a figure which changed little in the first millennium. From about the year 1000 the population increased to reach the critical threshold of one billion in about 1800. In 1930 two billion was reached; in 1960, three; in 1974, four and in 1990, five; so that by end of the second millennium the world's population will not be far off six billion. These figures make credible the view held among demographers that of all the people who have ever lived on the face of the Earth – going back to the origins of *Homo sapiens sapiens* some hundred thousand years ago – a remarkably high proportion were alive at some time or another in the twentieth century.

The proportion of all those who have ever lived who have observed solar eclipses from some point on the path of totality is almost certain to be considerably higher after the eclipse of 11 August 1999. One reason, which was already

196

established with the Indian eclipse of 1898, is the number of people who travel, often from far outside the path of totality, to vantage points located somewhere along it. This number will be particularly large in countries with a modern transport infrastructure and a population that can afford to make recreational use of it. It also helps if the population is concentrated along, or close to the path of totality.

Urbanisation is therefore another factor that can lead to a very large number of observers. In the Western industrial world, defined by Europe and North America, this was the characteristic demographic process of the nineteenth century. This was also the period, in these parts of the world, in which the demographic explosion led to cities whose populations were to be counted in millions – of which there were very few indeed before the year 1800. In the twentieth century, and particularly in its second half, the demographic explosion shifted to the developing countries: once again it was the cities that grew at an unprecedented rate, the vast, mainly impoverished populations living for the most part on the margins of society. No one at the beginning of the twentieth century would have thought that by its end Mexico City, would be the largest city in the world with a population approaching twenty million, and others such as São Paulo, Cairo, Karachi, Calcutta, Jakarta, Manila, Bangkok, Shanghai, Seoul and Tokyo not all that far behind. This list is by no means exhaustive.

The lesson is clear: for the largest possible number of observers, the path of totality should cover a large number of cities, above all in parts of the world where favourable economic factors make it possible for people, nor ordinarily living or working along the path of totality, to take time off to view the eclipse from some favourable vantage point along its path. In the entire history of eclipses, none satisfies these conditions better than that of 1999. Plymouth, Le Havre, Rouen, Amiens, Reims, Metz, Saarbrücken, Karlsruhe,

Stuttgart, Munich, Salzburg, Graz, Szeged, Bucharest, Mosul, Esfahan and Karachi all lie on the path of totality. The French towns are all in the densely populated industrial north-east of the country, those in Germany in the equally well developed south (where Bavaria is one of the most successful growth areas of the European Union). They all have at least a hundred thousand inhabitants; Munich, Bucharest and Esfahan have more than a million and Karachi (with its surrounding hinterland) more than ten million.

The experience of the eclipse is certain to be shared by millions of visitors from outside the path of totality: some – to judge from the travel brochures – will have crossed half the world to see it. In the south-west of England, a permanent population of about a million expects a sevenfold increase on the day itself – a boon for a popular holiday area. In France, the coast of Normandy, equally popular, should also do well. Here also, the close proximity of Paris (where the Charles de Gaulle airport is near the edge of the path) will provide the opportunity of experiencing totality to millions of people, many of whom are certain to take it – at least if the weather is fine. The same will be true of Vienna and Budapest – both capital cities with well over a million inhabitants. Taking all these factors to account, an estimate of a hundred million possible observers is not unreasonable.

How will all this compare with the other twentieth-century eclipses? The closest rival is probably 24 October 1995. Then the eclipse path began in Iran, crossed Afghanistan, Pakistan and India, a corner of the Indian Ocean, Burma, Thailand and Vietnam, to end by crossing the South China Sea into the Pacific Ocean. The greatest concentration of population along the path of totality was in India, in the vast, densely inhabited flood plain of the Ganges. The path of totality was narrow, about 50 km, and crossed only two large cities, Agra and Allahabad. Intensive agriculture in the flood plain supports a large rural population, but this is dispersed over the whole area. Counted in terms of place of work or place of abode – likely to be one and the same in rural India – only a small fraction of the population of the Ganges flood plain would have been on the path of totality. Given the narrowness of the path, thirty to forty million would be a reasonable figure here.

What of visitors from outside the path? On the day of the eclipse many offices closed, and the mobile middle classes had the opportunity to leave the large cities and seek out a vantage point on the path of totality, where conditions for observation were near-perfect. The main problem facing potential eclipse watchers was a transport system which was hardly able to support travel on the scale expected in England in 1999, and which in India cost far too much for the majority of the population to make use of it. The tens of thousands who still travelled, mainly by train, to see the eclipse were as nothing compared to the millions expected in the south-west of England in 1999.

The eclipse of 11 July 1991 is comparable. Its path crossed the capital cities of five countries: Mexico, Guatemala, El Salvador, Nicaragua and Costa Rica. The combined populations of these five countries is something over a hundred million, and of this number more than 80 per cent live in Mexico. The twenty million inhabitants of the capital city must have comprised at least half the observers, so for the whole country forty million would be an upper limit, with possibly ten million more from the other smaller countries along the path of totality.

In the earlier years of the twentieth century there were few eclipses to rival those of the 1990s. On 24 January 1925 the path of totality crossed densely populated areas in southern Ontario, New York State and southern New England. This, the most recent total eclipse experienced by Toronto and New York City, could just have been observed by fifty million, but hardly more, since in 1925 this would have been about a third of the population of the whole United States. A similar number could have observed the eclipse of 15 February 1961, which passed over southern France and northern Italy – both densely populated regions – to end up, after crossing Yugoslavia and Romania, in the thinly populated steppe and tundra of the Soviet Union. The eclipse of 20 June 1955, with an exceptionally wide path and long duration, would also have been experienced by tens of millions in mainland south-east Asia and the islands of the Philippines.

Just over a hundred years ago, the Indian eclipse of 22 January 1898 was probably observed by more people than any other previous eclipse, although those of 17 December 1870 and 28 July 1851 - both observed through much of Europe – may have rivalled it. In any case, we are moving back in time to a period when populations – particularly in cities – were much smaller, and the possibility of travel much more restricted. The total solar eclipse of 1715, where half of England and Wales (including London) lay along the path of totality, could have been observed by only two or three million in a country whose total population was barely five million. (This, London's last total eclipse, had the advantage of good weather throughout the country – unlike the last English eclipse, on 29 June 1927.)

The demographic record predicted for 1999 will probably not hold for long. Twenty-five years on, the total solar eclipse of 8 April 2024 will cross the United States from Texas to Maine, and include parts of Mexico and Canada. Dallas, St Louis, Cleveland, Buffalo and Toronto – to mention only five large cities – will all lie long the path, or close to it. It would be rash to predict how many people will take the opportunity to observe it, but given the world-wide interest in the 1999 eclipse, the record numbers expected for this year will almost certainly be exceeded a quarter of a century later.

9

Anthropologists and Travellers

The Anthropological Dilemma

Almost exactly a hundred years ago an expedition from Cambridge spent a year working in the islands of the Torres Straits, which separate Australia from New Guinea. The expedition, which has an almost mythological status in the history of social anthropology, established field-work as the basis for all future research. During the 'classical' period of twentieth-century anthropology (which included at least the first fifty years), it was accepted almost without question that the appropriate subject for research was a remote and homogeneous population, generally in some colonial territory, living in a state of complete cultural isolation. There was no question of communication, by means of the written word, with the outside world: the language spoken by such a population had never been reduced to writing, so that there was no record of its own history to be deciphered by archaeologists. The visible and material components of its culture were limited to what could be seen by the eye or touched by the hand within the confines of the local community. Outside lay an almost mythical world, comparable to the *terra incognita*, inhabited by dragons and other mythical beasts, portrayed by medieval map-makers. When the anthropologist came to his field-work among such an isolated population, he would often be the first outsider to bring knowledge of this other world.

The anthropologists of the Torres Straits generation are no longer with us. Even so, I have had any number of experiences in my own research areas – Mexico and Japan – which show that people can still be remarkably isolated from the cosmopolitan world that we take for granted. Among the remote Indian populations of the southern Mexican highlands I have talked to people who had never heard of the sea, and found it next to impossible to grasp what I told them about it. In remote mountain villages in Japan I have met people of my own generation who had never before talked with a foreigner – a species, known as *gaijin*, which might just as well come from another planet.

Anthropology is wary of generalisations. None the less, it is fair to say that the isolated populations, the study of which established the genre, combine an intensive knowledge of the local scene – its economy, infrastructure and society, plus its climate, topography and natural history – with an astonishing ignorance of everything outside. A written record of the botanical knowledge accumulated by the people of Zinacantan (adjacent to my own research area in Mexico) required two volumes of English text.[1] This knowledge extends, in detail, to areas such as ritual and medicine, outside the normal bounds of Western scientific botany. To a very large extent, it makes sense only because of its practical application. The fact that Tzotzil, the language of Zinacantan, is only spoken not written, means that the English text does not correspond to any permanent record kept by the people themselves. None the less, it still forms part of the cultural heritage of a population of the order of ten thousand.

Practically none of this knowledge came from outside: it was built up on the basis of plants growing within the clearly defined boundaries of Zinacantan. The informants who transmitted it to the American authors of the English record did so by word of mouth, with their own memories as their only resource.

When it comes to incorporating the heavens into any local culture, the picture changes radically. The people of Zinacantan, or any other local community, can hardly fail to realise that they share the heavens with people at the very edge of the world (however far away that may be), and from the very beginning of time. Nothing, however, can be made of the heavens unless they are domesticated – a process exemplified by dividing the stars into different constellations, whose richly evocative names transcend the here and now. As I write today (6 July 1998), in temperate Amsterdam, the easiest way for me to see a scorpion is to look south in the night sky an hour or two before midnight. The sky would certainly be the only place where I could see a dragon – an entirely mythical beast – and I would be able to see it throughout the hours of darkness. The names of these constellations, Scorpius and Draco, and those of many others, go back at least two thousand years, and are still used by astronomers.

For the people of Zinacantan, the significance of botany lies in its applications; for people almost everywhere the same is true of astronomy. The question is, how can any culture, having divided the stars in the night sky into different constellations, and noted also how the planets 'wander' through the constellations, then make use of this knowledge? One answer, going back beyond the earliest recorded history, is that the skies provide both a clock and a calendar: astronomical phenomena are the basis for the measurement of time on any scale – at least before the invention of the caesium clock. (Let us note, though, that

as a phenomenon a solar eclipse is no use for this purpose.)
Very few cultures stop at this point. To celestial phenomena are attributed meanings which go far beyond the
measurement of time. The indexes to the four volumes of
Claude Lévi-Strauss's *Introduction to a Science of Mythology*[2] list dozens of page references to the cluster of stars
known as the Pleiades (in the constellation Taurus), showing
its association with such diverse categories as fish cycles,
intestines, epidemics and poison. In some cases, such as fish
cycles, there may be a rational basis simply because fish, like
the Pleiades, have an annual season. Others, such as poison,
lack any such basis: so that the Amazonian belief that snakes
lose their venom with the annual disappearance of the Pleiades,[3] some time in April, has no scientific foundation.

We have seen in Chapter 2 how the irregularity of total
solar eclipses (which in any location occur, on average, once
every 375 years) makes them an event almost impossible to
record, systematically, in any pre-literate society. The most
that can be expected is that such an event, together with the
appropriate response to it, is stored in the collective folk
memory to become part of an oral tradition handed down
from one generation to another. On those rare occasions
when totality occurs twice in a relatively short period of
time (such as happened in the west of England in the early
eighteenth century), the oral tradition is likely to be
reinforced, and the prescribed means for dealing with a total
eclipse will become more deeply entrenched in the local
culture. This process can also be helped considerably by
having the eclipse lore incorporated into a genre sometimes
known as 'oral literature', incorporating 'myths, narratives,
epics, lyrics, praise poetry, laments and the verbal texts of
songs'.[4] This could well explain at least some of the cases of
solar eclipses examined by Lévi-Strauss in his *Introduction to
a Science of Mythology*.

That is about as far as it goes. As an event which the

cultural anthropologists, in principle, must take into account – at least if their monographs are to be complete – the solar eclipse is extremely problematic. Consequently, references to such an event in the hundreds of published monographs are few and far between. What, then, is the problem?

When it comes to field-work, there are two possible scenarios. In the first, anthropologists are actually in the field at the time of a solar eclipse. Then, particularly if they were working somewhere along the path of totality, they would hardly fail to notice how the people around them reacted to it. This does not mean that they will necessarily publish what they observe; although my intuition is that the few descriptions of such reactions to be found in the published literature come from anthropologists who, by pure chance, happened to be working in the field at the time of a solar eclipse. They would then have been well placed not only to observe how people react, but also to ask how they explain and interpret their experience. It may be that neither explanation nor interpretation is possible simply because no local tradition includes, even implicitly, such a phenomenon. The local population may simply lack the cultural resources to place what they are confronted with in any meaningful context.

This is at the opposite pole to the position of the hundreds of millions of people who will witness the 1999 eclipse, the overwhelming majority of whom will have the benefit of a history of eclipses, recorded in writing, going back some three thousand years. Except for the very few who will already have witnessed a total solar eclipse, 1999 will still hold some surprises, but the actual space and time coordinates will have been known long in advance and, available for consultation on, for example, the Internet. With the kind of populations described in the monographs published by anthropologists in the first half of the twentieth century, things were quite different. A field-worker fortunate enough to be present at the time of an eclipse was likely to witness the gut-reaction of people confronted by a one-off event which they could not relate to anything. (In the broad spectrum of twentieth-century anthropological research the instances recorded by Lévi-Strauss's *Introduction to a Science of Mythology* are very few and far between, and are in any case confined to the New World.) What such reactions proved to have in common was action intended either to bring a speedy end to the eclipse, or to ensure that it caused no permanent harm. Whatever form such action takes, events are bound to justify it: totality never lasts as long as eight minutes, and even the partial phase never lasts as long as three hours. Except as a psychological trauma, eclipses cause no harm to any natural species, including *Homo sapiens sapiens*.

Ideally, for every new eclipse of the Sun there should be some anthropologist with a research grant for investigating and recording the manifestations of local culture, along the path of totality, occurring as a reaction to it. Indeed, where the path is long, as in 1999, not one, but several anthropologists should be assigned this task. Some hope – the theme is much too marginal to meet the demands of those who control research funds. But this is a matter of perception, and one day some influential head of department just might allocate funds for a research student to research the local reactions to a solar eclipse. The problem is that the time dimension of eclipses does not fit the modus operandi of the discipline itself. A few minutes of intensive observation and recording may be a good pay-off for an eclipse astronomer, for the whole discipline of astronomy is used to reading a massive amount of theory into one simple event – just think of Einstein and the perihelion of Mercury. This is not consistent with the mind-cast of anthropologists, who expect results to be supported by a period of field-work measured in months, not minutes.

The second scenario is much more common than the first: the anthropologist learns about the place of eclipses in the local culture not by being present when one occurs, but by asking informants what they have learnt about eclipses in the course of their lives – which, in the best-case scenario, will actually include the direct experience of one of them. This is not, however, a line of investigation often followed by anthropologists, nor one to which their informants can often respond in any useful way. When it comes to explanation and interpretation, most of the recorded cases come from cultures with a long literate tradition – even though the actual literate classes may only be a small part of the population.

This has been a long introduction, but it was necessary to explain why the harvest from anthropology is so meagre. What, then, does it actually amount to? First, when it comes to spontaneous reactions, the most common counter-measure is simply to make a lot of noise (like the hotel staff in Mexico who disturbed the astronomers from the Royal Observatory of Belgium during the 1991 solar eclipse). The custom, according to Lévi-Strauss, has been recorded the world over. The noise can be culturally predetermined if a previous solar eclipse has some place in the folk memory – not all that likely, given that the average interval between solar eclipses at any one locality is 375 years. None the less, this does appear to happen. The Arawak of Guiana, for example, see a solar eclipse as a fight between the Sun and the Moon, and by uttering terrified cries they try to separate them.[5] Usually, however, the noise is to frighten away the animal or monster about to devour the Sun.[6] In other mythical scenarios, smoke may be an alternative to noise.[7]

As for explanations, the natural world is often projected onto the interaction between the Sun and Moon on the occasion of an eclipse. As already noted a number of times, the most widespread theme is simply that of the Sun being eaten. As a variant of this theme, the Bakairi of Brazil see a vast black bird, of the species *Crotophaga* (illustrated in Figure 9.1), hiding the Sun with its wings.[8] In other tribal communities sex, often as incest, provides the basis of explanation, sometimes with role-reversal: the Arapaho of the

Figure 9.1 *Crotophaga minor*, a South American bird believed to cause eclipses by eating the Sun.

great plains of North America see a solar eclipse as the Sun and Moon changing places in the sky.[9] The incestuous theme is particularly appropriate, given the essentially deviant character of an eclipse. The normal cycle of day and night, with the Sun as the male element alternating with the female Moon, is broken when the two come together in an eclipse, day becoming night then night becoming day once more.[10] Yin and yang as the basic ordering principle of the Universe is comparable to incest prohibition – one of the few principles common to almost all cultures known to anthropology.

Long-term adaptation to a dominant culture may change the position, as is shown by the picture of a solar eclipse in Figure 9.2. The artist, Marian López Calixto, was one of my informants when I conducted field-work in Mexico in the early 1970s. He made the drawing for a colleague of

Figure 9.2 A solar eclipse as interpreted by Marian López Calixto, a Chamula Indian, in terms of the crucifixion. In local tradition Christ is identified with the Sun. He describes his pictures in these words: 'Here is Our Lord Sun/Christ. They are killing him there in the sky. They have bound him to a tree and are killing him. He is about dead.' the other figures in the picture are demons devouring the blood of Christ.

mine, Gary Gossen, who has published an exhaustive study[11] of the way the people of Chamula – Marian's own tribe – conceive of the world, both natural and supernatural. The picture is significant for its identification of Christ with the Sun (which is standard in the Chamula cosmology), so that a solar eclipse equates with the crucifixion. The picture shows Jesus nailed to a tree, a common surrogate for the cross in the Christian tradition, and the question is why Marian saw this in terms of an eclipse. The answer, most probably, is to be found in the fact that the Chamula also identify the Virgin Mary with the Moon, which would fit well with the disturbance of the yin–yang principle by an eclipse, and would even suggest a violation of the incest prohibition. In Marian's picture there is a lot more than meets the eye.

In contrast to the historical record, that of anthropology contains little suggesting any cultural recognition of untoward consequences of an eclipse. At the level of classical Torres Straits anthropology, leading figures are also prey to untimely death, but I have discovered no such death being attributed to an eclipse. With one exception, that of the Ingalik of northern Canada, I have also failed to find any instance of what might be called post-operative treatment following an eclipse.

The problem with the Ingalik is that the brief ethnographic record[12] does not make clear what parts of it apply to solar as opposed to lunar eclipses, which are its main focus. In this case, the shamans are clearly responsible for the appropriate ritual, and it is believed that if they fail to carry it out correctly they will die within two days. Just as with the astrologers at the court of Nebuchadnezzar, it pays to get it right. The shamans' ritual obligation is to ensure the safe return to Earth, from the 'house of the moon', of all the animals and fish which disappear at the time of an eclipse. The ritual requires all the men to take their weapons, and a sack containing every kind of fish and meat from every kind of animal that has gone to the Moon, and go to the down-river end of the village, from where they proceed to circle the village in the direction of the Sun. Once the circuit is completed the sacks are emptied, and the fish and meat cut up into small pieces which are passed round for all the participants to eat.

The Ingalik rite is part of a culture (typical of north-

210

eastern Canada) that is dominated by the relation between men who hunt and the animals hunted by them. Success in hunting depends upon communication between hunter and hunted, both during their life and after their death, and this was mediated by the shamans. Calvin Martin suggests 'how the exploitation of game for subsistence appears to have been regulated by the hunter's continued attentiveness to the welfare of his prey – both living and dead, it is immaterial'.[13] The behaviour of animals during a solar eclipse reflects a want of attention by the hunters, and only the shamans can regain the trust of the animals. The ritual described in the previous paragraph is the means of achieving this end, which is essential if successful hunting is to be resumed.

Eclipse travellers

Captain James Cook (1728–1779), the greatest navigator in maritime history, was also the first great eclipse traveller. Sailing with the schooner *Greville*, bought for him in the summer of 1763 and his first independent command, he experienced his first solar eclipse, observed from one of the Burgeo islands off the coast of Newfoundland, on 5 August 1766. His interest in eclipses had been aroused by Charles Leadbetter's *Compleat System of Astronomy*, a book whose author, with a passion for eclipses, had proclaimed how a

> person being well skill'ed in Astronomy, he may, by the knowledge of Eclipses . . . determine the true Difference of Meridians between *London*, and the Meridian where the ship then is; which reduced to Degrees and Minutes of the Equator, is the true Longitude found at Sea.[14]

Once the coordinates recorded by Cook had been received in London, were they compared with those recorded at Oxford for the same eclipse by the Rev. Hornsby, and communicated by Dr John Bevis, a physician, to the Royal Society. The object of the comparison was to 'compute . . . the Difference of Longitude of the places of observation' and it showed how remarkably accurate Cook's reckoning was – only three miles (5 km) out across the whole width of the Atlantic. This was a decisive moment in the life of Cook. It was the first time that his work had come to the notice of the Royal Society, which would support his subsequent voyages and finally elect him as a member on 29 February 1776.

By this time, Cook had already observed two further solar eclipses. One, on 10 May 1771, was observed off Ascension Island in the South Atlantic when he was returning from his first voyage to the Pacific – famous in the history of astronomy for his observation, from Tahiti, of the transit of Venus on 3 June 1769. The other, during his second voyage to the Pacific, was observed on 6 September 1774 off New Caledonia. In the last three years of his life he was to observe two more, on 5 July 1776 from Tonga and on 30 December 1777 from the appropriately named Eclipse Island. (This little island, now called Cook Islet, is just off the coast of Christmas Island, first visited by Cook a week earlier and named by him after the season of its discovery.) During almost the whole of this period Cook had the advantage of being the first explorer of the oceans to be able to use the *Nautical Almanac*, first published in 1766 for events in the following year, 1767.

This meant that for the rest of his seafaring life (which ended when he was murdered on Hawaii on 14 February 1779) he had a completely reliable and accurate guide to the positions of the Sun, the Moon, the planets and the stars, for any time and from any location where he happened to be – which could be almost any part of the world. Where the almanac recorded the same coordinates for both Sun and Moon, there would be a solar eclipse. From the time of his second Pacific voyage (1772–5), Cook also had the advantage of John Harrison's H-4 marine chronometer, which, used in conjunction with the abridged version of the *Nautical Almanac*, made navigation simpler and safer than it had ever been before.

The period from Cook's first observation of a solar eclipse on the 5 August 1766 to his last on 30 December 1777 was just over eleven years. To observe five solar eclipses – one in the North Atlantic, one in the South Atlantic and three in the South Pacific – in so short a period would be a remarkable achievement even today, when eclipse astronomers and eclipse tourists have the advantage of jet travel; in the eighteenth century it was simply stupendous. At the time of his death, he had beyond doubt observed more solar eclipses than any other man in history.

The nineteenth century saw eclipse travel transformed by the use of the steam engine for locomotion by both land and sea. By 1850 almost any eclipse was accessible to observation, provided that preparations were begun sufficiently far in advance of the date. By this time also, astronomers not only had good scientific reasons for wanting to observe solar eclipses, but also, with the invention of photography, possessed the means to record their observations. An early high point was the observation by professional astronomers in many parts of Europe, of the eclipse of 28 July 1851 – just in time for a photograph of the Sun's corona to be displayed at the Great Exhibition in London. The first to observe this eclipse was the French astronomer Antoine d'Abbadie, who took an expedition to Frederiksvoern in Norway.

Eclipse expeditions continued through the second half of the nineteenth century until well into the twentieth. Many were organised by the Greenwich Observatory, in a period of history when the Astronomer Royal had a much greater interest in solar eclipses than any late-twentieth-century holder of that office. In the years around the turn of the century, Walter Maunder, a dedicated eclipse traveller, published three long accounts of the eclipse expeditions he mounted to Norway in 1896, India in 1898, and Spain and Portugal in 1900. The first was a disaster, because bad weather in Norway precluded any useful observations. The second expedition, to India, had to make a radical change of plan at the last moment since the sites initially chosen for observation were in a part of the country infected by plague. The third had to contend with the fact that Spain was at war. Life is never that straightforward for eclipse travellers.

The Indian eclipse, on 22 January 1898, may be seen – in spite of the plague – as a fitting climax to nineteenth-century eclipse travel. The English party's stay in India opened ominously, since Colonel Goodyer Adye, who had been appointed to help them (and 'had the reputation of being one of the most experienced men in India in the knowledge of the native languages and ways'[15]), having met the party when it disembarked at Bombay, died within the week. In spite of this unhappy beginning, observations were made and photographs taken from three different locations. One of these, Jeur, witnessed the beginning of mass eclipse tourism, and the description by the party's Henry Cousens is too good to leave out:

Whilst the serious work was thus going on at the eclipse camp, Jeur station and its surroundings were rapidly putting on a holiday appearance. A month or so previously some one suggested that the railway company should run a special from Bombay to Poona, which, after some hesitation, they advertised to start if a sufficient number applied for seats beforehand. Not one, but eight long specials steamed into Jeur on the eclipse morning from Bombay,

214

Poona, Ahmadnagar, Hyderabad, Baroda and Madras, and emptied out hundreds of European and native visitors, some keen on observing the eclipse and the astronomers, others out more for a picnic and the fun of the thing ... Scores of white tents crowded around the station and peeped out from the surrounding trees. The goods shed was converted into a great refreshment-room, and covers were set in first-class style for three hundred, but the majority of the visitors had brought their own tiffin baskets. The shed was gaily decorated with flags, bunting, evergreens and Chinese lanterns. A special Government telegraph office was the only sign of business. Jeur had never before seen so much of the Western world, and, if the astronomers are correct, it will be a very long time ere it will see it again.[16]

The Indian eclipse of 1898 also attracted an unprecedented number of pious Hindus to the holy city of Benares, who saw the occasion as exceptionally auspicious for bathing in the River Ganges. In Calcutta a blind man was reputed to hear the eclipse, and in Cawnpore a Brahmin predicted an earthquake. Once the eclipse had safely passed, Jeur was not the only village to spend the evening *en fête*.

The English eclipse of 29 June 1927 also attracted much interest, even though the path of totality crossed the country before 6 a.m. Special coach and train excursions were laid on, and in London, which would enjoy 96 per cent partiality, the parks were opened ahead of time. The weather was a wash-out, however, so thousands of people were disappointed. The Astronomer Royal, Sir Frank Dyson, and his party were not among them: they had chosen to set up their instruments in the grounds of Giggleswick School, in the middle of the Pennines. This proved to be about the only place with fine weather, and to this day eclipse astronomers talk of the luck of Giggleswick.

Until the jet age of the 1960s and after, eclipse tourists tended not to travel far, so the number of observers – apart from astronomers – depended largely on what large centres of population lay on the path of totality. In Thailand, tens of millions witnessed the eclipse of 8 May 1948 because the path of totality not only crossed the country from one side to the other, but also included its capital, Bangkok. Further tens of millions witnessed it in China and Korea, but relatively few can have made a special journey to see it.

In the last thirty odd years of the twentieth century, jet travel has established eclipse tourism on a world-wide basis. A Florida travel agency, Scientific Expeditions Inc., has been organising package tours to solar eclipse locations for the last 25 years, and with every eclipse demand increases. A British travel agency, Explorers Tours, offers four packages, for Cornwall, Romania, Turkey and Iran for the 11 August 1999. A cohort of eclipse freaks numbering several hundred now travels the world, making sure not to miss out on a single solar eclipse, though probably relatively few made it to the eclipse visible from Siberia on 9 March 1997. Many others are bound to be disappointed: those who went to the big island of Hawaii for the eclipse of 11 July 1991 were let down by bad weather resulting from the recent volcanic eruption of Mount Pinatubo in the Philippines. Only the select few who were above the weather, at the top of Mauna Kea, enjoyed the eclipse. Ordinary tourists were not among them: the summit of the mountain, the site of some of the world's most advanced observatories, is a restricted area.

The astronomers have also joined the jet set. The vast encampments set up in the first half of the twentieth century, with squads of locally recruited labour, now belong to a different age. All the instrumentation now required, digitalized even down to the cameras, can be checked in as ordinary passenger baggage on scheduled flights.

The eclipse in literature

In March 1998 a print-out of currently available book titles which incorporated the word 'eclipse' listed nearly fifty books, of which the great majority had nothing to do with actual eclipses, whether of the Sun or the Moon. This harvest is considerably greater than that produced by a correspondence in *The Times* on the occasion of the 1927 eclipse, when totality was last observed from England. This threw up little beyond the famous 'eclipse' chapter in Rider Haggard's *King Solomon's Mines*, a book which on its first publication in 1885 was described by the *Athenaeum* as 'one of the best books for boys – old or young – which we remember to have read'. The original text of *King Solomon's Mines* is still in print;[17] now, at the end of the twentieth century, it is ripe for deconstruction. It is a good starting point for looking at the theme of eclipses in literature.

The book exploited a formula already well established in nineteenth-century literature by such well-known authors as R. M. Ballantyne, G. A. Henty and Robert Louis Stevenson. It belonged to a genre defined by 'stories . . . exploiting the appeal of exotic parts of the [British] Empire, such as Africa and India, and based upon an unquestioning assumption of British superiority over all foreigners, especially natives'.[18] *King Solomon's Mines* focused upon a fictitious southern African kingdom, Kukuanaland, which was obviously ready for incorporation into the British Empire.

The tale is told by Allen Quatermain, who has joined two others, Sir Henry Curtis and Captain John Good, in an expedition into the dark interior of Africa. Their purpose is to find Allen's younger brother George, who disappeared while searching for the fabled King Solomon's Mines. True to the genre, the expedition has a native guide, Umbopa, while its destination, Kukuanaland, is ruled by a bloodthirsty tyrant, Twala, advised by an old witch, Gagool. Once within the kingdom, the expedition encounters the leader of a rival faction, the Infadoos, who would gladly see the king deposed. The only problem is that he would then be succeeded by his son, Scragga, who promises to be even more tyrannical. At the critical moment it turns out that Umbopa is the rightful king, having fled the kingdom with his mother (the wife of Twala's predecessor) when he was a baby. This gives him the right to be called Ignosi (or 'Lord'), and the local chiefs are prepared to rally round the Infadoos, in support of Ignosi, provided they receive some supernatural confirmation of Ignosi's legitimacy.

The solution is provided by Captain Good. On the evening of 3 June, he reads from his almanac '4 June, total eclipse of the Sun commences at 11.15 Greenwich time, visible in these Islands – *Africa, &c.*'. This would be the sign required by the local chiefs. The next morning, Quatermain calls them together and addresses them, making use of his secret knowledge:

> I tell you that this day, one hour after mid-day, will be put out [the] sun for a space of an hour, and darkness shall cover the earth, and it shall be for a sign that we are indeed men of honour, and that Ignosi is indeed King of the Kukuanas. If we do this, will it satisfy ye?[19]

The chiefs acknowledged that they would be satisfied. Everything goes as planned: Twala's court, including Gagool, is routed in confusion as total darkness descends in the early afternoon. The solar eclipse proves to be the turning point in the fortunes of the king; Scragga, son and heir, is left dead, impaled on his own spear.

In an age when eclipses no longer held any secrets from sophisticated English astronomers, the eclipse chapter in *King Solomon's Mines* was to cause its author no end of trouble. Scientifically, everything possible was wrong about it. To begin with, there was a full Moon the night before the eclipse, and a solar eclipse can occur only at new Moon. Then totality lasted for the impossibly long period of 'an hour or more'. And finally, the path of totality can never cover both 'these [British] Islands' and southern Africa.

The pity of it is that if Rider Haggard had done his homework, he could have avoided all these mistakes. In later editions the chapter was rewritten, with a lunar eclipse replacing the solar one, but the loss of dramatic effect was considerable. Still, the chapter lost none of its effect on readers in imperial Britain. Its essential message is that the British are not only more honest than other races, they are also smarter (even though Rider Haggard's understanding of eclipses was not so smart). This demonstration of racial superiority went down just as well in the United States, where *King Solomon's Mines* enjoyed phenomenal sales. It also provided the model for a story by an author even better known than Rider Haggard – Mark Twain, whose *A Connecticut Yankee in King Arthur's Court* used a solar eclipse to show how the ancient Brits could be outsmarted by a good Yankee any day of the week.

In Chapter 6, 'The Eclipse', the Yankee hero is about to be burnt at the stake in the presence of the king and queen and all their court, with Merlin the magician about to set light to the faggots. What the man from late-nineteenth-century Connecticut knew, but not the king and his courtiers, was that at the critical moment a solar eclipse would supervene. As the darkness increased, and the courtyard fell under the path of totality, the eclipse was seen as a threat, brought about by the impending *auto-da-fé*, which only its intended victim could stave off. *The Connecticut Yankee*, like the three heroes of *King Solomon's Mines*, claimed the power to end the eclipse, but in return for doing so he exacted the price of his own freedom – which was willingly granted. He got the idea from his knowledge of history:

> You see, it was the eclipse. It came into my mind, in the nick of time, how Columbus, or Cortez, or one of those people, played an eclipse as a saving trump once, on some savages, and I saw my chance. I could play it myself, now; and it wouldn't be any plagiarism, either, because I should get it in nearly a thousand years ahead of those parties.[20]

The Connecticut Yankee was nowhere as successful as other books by Mark Twain, such as *Huckleberry Finn* or *Tom Sawyer*, but it was well received as a political tract bashing the British, and particularly their aristocracy. A reviewer from California, writing in the *Woodland Democrat*, saw the book as a 'forcible arraignment of the English nobility for its oppression of the people' and noted that 'No one will fail to catch the spirit of Democratic independence, right and justice, which is manifested on every page'.[21]

In the twentieth century a scenario structurally identical to those in *King Solomon's Mines* and the *Connecticut Yankee* is to be found in the realm of the comic strip. In *The Sun Temple*,[22] Tintin, after a series of adventures in the Andes (highly improbable but characteristic of his way of life), ends up, with his three companions, tied to the stake by the Incas and waiting for the faggots to be set alight. At this critical moment he implores the Sun god Pachamac to let his brilliant face be veiled as a sign of disapproval of the impending sacrifice. The expected solar eclipse happens, and the Incas implore Tintin to beseech the Sun to shine again. Once again the hero, crowned with success, is released, but in this case – so far as I know – no one has attempted to draw a moral from the story.

The same is not true of a much more recent book, Phil Whitaker's *Eclipse of the Sun*, whose focus is the Indian eclipse of 24 October 1995. The leitmotiv of the book is the conflict between modern and traditional in the small Indian town of Nandrapur, played out against the background of the impending eclipse. The leading character, Rajesh Deshpande, teaches science in the local secondary school and plans to exploit the eclipse as a spectacle which will make him rich. In collaboration with his friend Mukerjee, the local doctor, he selects a site at the edge of the village. There, for a small admission fee, people will be able to witness totality in optimal conditions, with special dark glasses made of exposed X-ray film no longer needed by Dr Mukerjee. Deshpande, whose favourite reading is the weekly *Rational Recorder*, also gives a series of lectures (with, once again, a fee charged for admission), preparing Nandrapur for the expected eclipse.

Whereas Deshpande and Mukerjee represent the modern side of Indian life, Deshpande's wife, Sumila, anxious to conceive a child, is on the traditional side, which also includes Basak Baba, a popular local guru who is supported by a whole cohort of *sadhus* – devotees of his own particular cult. It would be unfair to give away the book's denouement, which comes, needless to say, with the eclipse itself. Suffice to say that it provides the occasion for a confrontation between Deshpande and Basak Baba – which, as described by Whitaker, reflects a distinctively 'orientalist' view of modern India. However hard they try, Indians do better to stick to their own traditions, allowing such men as Basak Baba to claim that they can save 'the town of Nandrapur from evil and malign spirits, [and] *prevent* the eclipse',[23] rather than to allow men such as Deshpande and Mukerjee to propagate and exploit their own half-digested version of modern Western science.

Whitaker's book is highly evocative, and its portrayal of society in a small town in contemporary India is extraordinarily convincing. In a sense it is Kipling brought up to

date, and to know what that means it is instructive to read
Edward Said's introduction to a recent edition of *Kim*. Said
made his name with a book entitled simply *Orientalism*. Its
object was 'to show that European culture gained in strength
and identity by setting itself off against the Orient as a sort
of surrogate and even underground self.'[24] When it comes to
eclipses, this process started with Matteo Ricci's remarkable
mission to China in the sixteenth century (which Said himself fails to note). It was to lead eventually to the conviction,
which came to be held throughout Europe, of a cultural
leadership, an idea of Europe as 'a collective notion identifying "us" Europeans against all "those" non-Europeans
. . . the idea of European identity as a superior one in comparison with all the non-European peoples and cultures'.[25]
In his introduction to *Kim*, Said cites Edmund Wilson's
judgement that 'we have been shown two entirely different
worlds existing side by side, with neither really understanding the other',[26] and that is precisely what Whitaker does in
Eclipse of the Sun, published nearly a century after *Kim*.

Pauline Melville's *The Ventriloquist's Tale*[27] flies in the
face of two sentences from Julian Barnes which she quotes
at the beginning of the book: 'There shall be no more novels
about incest. No, not even ones in very bad taste.' Her novel
is not only about incest, but also about the 'Einstein' eclipse
of 1919, and its theme is defined by a quotation from Claude
Lévi-Strauss:

> There is a myth which is known throughout the whole of
> the Americas from southern Brazil to the Baring Strait
> via Amazonia and Guiana and which establishes a direct
> equivalence between eclipses and incest.[28]

The action of *The Ventriloquist's Tale* takes place among
the remote populations of the savannah country of southern
British Guyana. Pauline Melville's ability to evoke the local

scene, in a quite different part of the world, is just as great as Phil Whitaker's. The axis of her book is provided by an incestuous and passionate brother–sister relationship which reaches its climax during the short period of totality of the 1919 eclipse. The involved and generally disastrous consequences of this relationship define the main story-line. Although this is a brilliant book, which rightly won the Whitbread First Novel Award in 1997, to any anthropologist it is pure fantasy – which adds to rather than detracts from its appeal.

Next to the works of fiction in which an actual solar eclipse plays a key role in the plot, there are others, often incorporating the word 'eclipse' in the title, in which the reference is metaphorical. A modern example is J. Bernlef's *Eclips*,[29] first published in Dutch in 1993. The whole of the action, which lasts little over a week, begins when the narrator, Kees Somer, losing control of the left side of his body, drives his car off the road into a *vaart*, one of the many inland waterways which criss-cross Holland. Like any Dutchman, Kees Somer knows how to rescue himself from this situation, but when he scrambles back onto dry land, he leaves not only his car at the bottom of the *vaart*, but the whole of his familiar, everyday world. He enters a new world in which he is completely disoriented – a netherworld defined by building sites, wrecked car-lots, run-down smallholdings and, finally, the village where he spent his own childhood. No one knows him, and those who look after him are way outside the mainstream of modern Dutch society. His life before plunging, with his car, into the *vaart* is seen only in flashbacks. He is incapacitated, mentally as well as physically, by the loss of one half of his body, but eventually his faculties return. He is finally found by the police, a drifter on a beach near his home, and his wife comes to fetch him. Life is set to return to normal, except that no one, including its owner, knows where to find the car.

The title 'Eclipse' is well-chosen for this psycho-romance. As with any solar eclipse, the ordinary world dissolves, to be replaced for a short time by an unreal world which does not accord with any previous experience. To anyone living in Holland the book is extremely evocative: the two worlds portrayed both ring true. It must have been a considerable challenge to the English translator to carry this over into another culture.

Total Eclipse is the title of a film script by Christopher Hampton,[30] based on the relationship between two nineteenth-century French poets, Paul Verlaine and Arthur Rimbaud, and Mathilde Verlaine, Paul's wife; Arthur's wife Isabelle plays no more than a supporting role. Any configuration of the Sun, the Moon and the Earth is an obvious model for a triangular relationship, and a *total eclipse* is equally appropriate to describe the situation in which one player, Arthur, completely supplants another, Paul, in the affections of a third, Mathilde.

It would be tedious to go through all the fifty-odd current titles that include the word 'eclipse'. Most of them, such as *The Eclipse of Council Housing*,[31] are simply banal. What is more, they often have no need of the nuances implied by the word 'eclipse' – so that *The Decline of Council Housing* would be a more appropriate title. One title, *Me and My Baby View the Eclipse*,[32] is just cute, but I have been unable to track it down this side of the Atlantic.

One book, Tony Walter's *Eclipse of Eternity*,[33] subtitled *A Sociology of the Afterlife*, not only uses the metaphor of an eclipse in an entirely appropriate way but also discusses an extremely interesting and relevant subject. The essence of a solar eclipse is to deprive the world (or that part of it along the path of totality) of its source of light: it is a radical impoverishment of everyday life, only acceptable because it is of such short duration. Tony Walter's theme is that something has happened, at some time in the last half century, to deprive at least part of the world of its vision of eternity: there is, indeed, a path of totality (passing right across my home-town of Amsterdam), along which this deprivation is more or less complete – at least in the closing years of the present millennium. Even in modern Christian life, 'eternity' has become an 'optional extra'.[34] If the eclipse metaphor is accurate, then of course eternity will regain its place in the consciousness of Christians: a mere eclipse lasting a half century odd is nothing to eternity.

The great virtue of Walter's book is that it exploits to the full its chosen metaphor, while accepting the inherent restrictions. The following passage is exemplary:

I simply observe that the heavenly realms seem to have disappeared from public life and from everyday life, if not from private belief, and I ask whether this heavenly light is no longer seen because it has been extinguished by secular ideas or because it has been eclipsed by practical concerns. If the latter, we must ask how total is the eclipse, how long it is likely to last, and whether it casts its shadow over the whole Earth or just over a few countries in the West.[35]

Later on, Walter considers the evidence that the 'eclipse is partial or that belief in eternity is emerging out of the eclipse', asking at the same time whether 'near death experiences, . . . beliefs about reincarnation, and in appearances of the dead . . . are the dramatic corona that so often flares around a total eclipse'.[36] At the same time he accepts the possibility of a postmodern age in which 'a new experience of eternity is being discovered, or rediscovered'.[37] Of course, only 'rediscovery' would fully justify the eclipse metaphor, for we know that in the long term eclipses change nothing.

At the end of this section, we are left to wonder what undiscovered treasures still remain to illustrate its theme, the eclipse in literature. Sheridan Williams, in his *UK Solar Eclipses from Year 1: An Anthology of 3,000 Years of Solar Eclipses* – a title which casts some doubt on the author's sense of British history – includes eleven quotations from English literature, starting with Shakespeare, having stated that there 'must be thousands of such mentions'.[38] I am doubtful. The same quotations come up again and again in all the obvious sources, the *Oxford Dictionary of Quotations* providing the richest harvest (and the *Larousse de Citations* nothing at all). Whether as a sign, a metaphor or an astronomical event, the range of a solar eclipse is remarkably restricted, and in writing this book I do not think I have missed anything important.

Taking two of the passages quoted by Williams, from Shakespeare's *King Lear*,

These late eclipses in the Sun and Moon portend no good to us[39]

and from Milton's *Paradise Lose*,

As when the Sun new-risen
Looks through the horizontal misty air
Shorn of his beams, or, from behind the Moon
In dim eclipse, disastrous twilight sheds
On half the nations, and with fear of change
Perplexes monarchs[40]

we encounter a theme which goes back to the furthest reaches of the ancient world of China and the Middle East. A solar eclipse is an event so out of the ordinary that it can be interpreted only as a portent. This is the traditional as opposed to the modern interpretation. The conflict between the two appears in six lines of verse, quoted by the *Aberdeen Observer* of 20 May 1836 in an article describing the eclipse of five days earlier, whose author I have been unable to trace:

> High on her speculative tower.
> Stood science waiting for the hour
> The sun was destined to endure
> That darkening of his radiant face,
> Which superstition strove to chace,
> Erewhile with rites impure.

No more need be said to end this chapter, and the book.

Notes

Chapter 1 The Eclipse as Phenomenon

1. G. B. Airy, 'On the results of recent calculations on the eclipse of Thales and the eclipses connected with it', in *Royal Institution Library of Science*, Vol. 1, *Astronomy* (Royal Institution, 1853), pp. 8–15.
2. Matthew xxvii.45. (All biblical references in this book are to the Revised Standard Version.)
3. The corona can be observed at other times by using an instrument known as a coronagraph, which is essentially a telescope incorporating a disc which hides the Sun's photosphere.
4. This phrase is the title of a book by the American language specialist Philip Liebermann: *Uniquely Human* (Harvard University Press, 1991).
5. The dates and paths of eclipses are taken from Sheridan Williams, *UK Solar Eclipses from the Year 1* (Clock Tower Press, Leighton Buzzard, 1996). There is no other time in this period of nearly 2,000 years in which two total solar eclipses were visible in the British Isles within so short a time of each other.

Chapter 2 The Celestial Dynamics of Eclipses

1. In this book 'billion' is used to mean 'thousand million', rather than the older British meaning of 'million million'.
2. Charon is larger in relation to Pluto, 'but the Pluto–Charon double system does not seem to represent a true planet–moon combination' (John Gribbin, *Companion to the Cosmos* (Phoenix, 1997), p. 331).
3. There is a small secular (long-term) variation in this angle of 8'.
4. Named after the Dutch astrophysicist Jan Oort (1900–1992), who first suggested its existence in the 1950s.
5. The astronomer and geographer Ptolemy (2nd century AD), who worked at Alexandria, wrote a thirteen-volume description of the Universe known as the *Almagest* in which he listed forty-eight constellations.
6. This is true over any historical time-span, given that recorded astronomy covers only the most recent millionth part of the lifetime of the Solar System. On a truly cosmic time-scale, however, the constellations are far from constant because the stars all have their own motions in space. Some of the familiar shapes will be quite different in, say, 100,000 years' time.
7. Given that the Sun appears to an observer to move from east to west, there is an element of paradox here. A simple experiment resolves the paradox. Place a light in the middle of a room to represent the Sun, then look at it and turn your head anticlockwise. The light will appear to move from east to west, imitating the course of the Sun as observed during the day. Next, walk round the lamp in an anticlockwise direction and look at it against the wall directly opposite. Relative to the wall, the light will then be seen to move from west to east, tracing the course of the Sun as it moves across the heavens in its own orbit.
8. By convention the prominent stars in each constellation are named, in order of brightness, after the letters of the Greek alphabet.
9. The Greek word means simply 'indicator'.
10. There are occasional instances of eclipses that change from annular to total.
11. This must not be confused with the length, 27.32 days, of the

sidereal month. The relation between the two is explained in Chapter 7.

12. The orbital inclination of Pluto's moon Charon is close to 90°.

13. An ellipse always has two foci. In a system of orbiting bodies, one focus is occupied by the body being orbited and the other is empty. Eccentricity is a measure of the ratio between the distance between the foci and the size of the ellipse. This ratio is zero when the two foci coincide, so that the ellipse becomes a circle. Because (with the exception of Pluto) the orbits of the planets in the Solar System are quite small, they can be treated as circular as a first approximation.

14. In the early nineteenth century, the German astronomer Friedrich Bessel (1784–1846) devised a scheme for characterising eclipses according to eight 'Besselian elements'. These parameters provide the rigorous mathematical basis for predicting eclipses, but the mathematics is too involved to go into here.

15. The point at which the Sun, in the course of its journey along the ecliptic, crosses the celestial equator from south to north.

16. This angle, known as the obliquity of the ecliptic, is currently decreasing by 46.85" per century. If it were to continue to decrease at this rate, then in some 180,000 years' time the plane of the earth's equator would come to coincide with the plane of the ecliptic. The differences between the seasons would then disappear, with dramatic consequences for the natural rhythms of life on our planet. But this will not happen because the inclination of the Earth's axis of rotation – and thus the obliquity of the ecliptic – fluctuates between 22° and 25° over a cycle that lasts for about 41,000 years.

17. The fact that the relative positions of the Sun, Earth and Moon are constantly changing as the Moon moves in its orbit around the Earth means that the combined gravitational force of the Sun and the Moon (to which the Moon's contribution is twice the Sun's) must vary, between fixed limits, over time. The rate of precession thus varies as well, but by a very small amount, so that over the complete cycle of 25,800 years it may be regarded as constant.

18. Strictly this is an approximation since it fails to take into account that the Earth's orbit is elliptical rather than circular. But the

231

eccentricity is small, so the approximation is sufficient for this calculation.

19. 11 hours = 0.46 days, and 0.46 × 60.87' = 28'.

Chapter 3 The Prehistoric Conundrum

1. For any bright star, there will be a certain day of the year on which it is first visible to the naked eye as it rises in the pre-dawn twilight just before sunrise. This was in ancient times referred to as the star's heliacal rising.
2. This statement has caused me some difficulty, but it is based upon a close reading of John North's *Stonehenge: Neolithic Man and the Cosmos* (HarperCollins, 1996), pp. 282–5.
3. In the 2 April 1998 issue of *Nature*, J. McKim Malville and colleagues reported the discovery, in the Nabta Playa depression of southern Egypt, of megaliths that have been dated to 2800 BC, making them considerably older than the Stonehenge monoliths. Made of sandstone, they are set out in three rows, a circle, and one free-standing monolith. In the circle there has been identified an orientation with the direction of sunrise at midsummer, while the isolated stone is seen as a symbol of male fertility. Compared with Stonehenge the complex is extremely small, and its investigation has only just begun.
4. See, for example, Fred Hoyle, *From Stonehenge to Modern Astronomy* (Cambridge University Press, 1971).
5. North, *Op. cit.*, p. 407.
6. Alexander Marshack, 'Lunar notations on Upper Paleolithic remains', *Science*, 1964, Vol. 146, pp. 743–5.
7. Bryan Brewer, *Eclipse* (Earth View, Seattle, 1991), pp. 9–10.

Chapter 4 The Premodern History of Eclipses

1. This usage of the word 'civilisation', although well established in the nineteenth century, has become less fashionable in the present postmodern age.
2. Denise Schmandt-Besserat, 'The earliest precursor of writing', *Scientific American*, June 1979, pp. 38–47. In fairness it should

be noted that some scholars, notably John de Francis in his *Visible Speech: The Oneness of Writing Systems* (University of Hawaii Press, 1989), p. 74, reject the view I adopt and see the *bullae* as a dead-end in the history of writing.

3. Eleanor Robson, personal communication (1998).

4. The material in this section on Babylon comes almost entirely from F. R. Stephenson's *Historical Eclipses and Earth's Rotation* (Cambridge University Press, 1997), Chapters 4–7.

5. Conversion tables from the Babylonian to the Julian calendar have been prepared for the entire period from 626 BC to AD 75.

6. There is only one perfect system for writing numbers: the place-value system of what we now call Arabic numerals. A place-value system is one in which the value indicated by a given numeral depends on its position in the number in which it appears. In the ancient world both the Babylonian and the Chinese systems can be seen as precursors of place value, but the first proper system appeared in India. The first known text to incorporate the system is the *Lokavibhaga*, written in Sanskrit and dating from the year AD 458 – long after the cuneiform numerals of Babylon had fallen into disuse. The numerals used in the Arab world derived directly from the Indian ones. For a fuller treatment, see my *The Anthropology of Numbers* (Cambridge University Press, 1991), pp. 45–6.

7. The full references, together with a discussion, are to be found in G. S. Kirt *et al.*, *The Pre-Socratic Philosophers*, 2nd edition (Cambridge University Press, 1983), pp. 81–3.

8. *Ibid.*, p. 82.

9. Pliny, *Naturalis historia*, translated by H. Rackham (Heinemann, 1938), II, 53.

10. Otto Neugebauer, *History of Ancient Mathematical Astronomy* (Springer, 1975), p. 604.

11. Stephenson, *Op. cit.*, p. 344.

12. Hippolytus, *Refutatio* 1, 8, 3–10, cited by Kirk *et al.*, *op. cit.*, p. 381.

13. Plutarch, *Moralia*, translated by H. Cherniss and W. C. Helmbold (Heinemann, 1957), Vol. XII, pp. 117–19.

14. Cited, in English translation, by J. K. Fotheringham, 'A solution of ancient eclipses of the Sun', *Monthly Notices of the Royal Astronomical Society*, 1920, Vol. 81, pp. 104–26.

15. Stephenson, *op. cit.*, p. 218.
16. In Japan this form of oracle is still used in connection with the installation of a new emperor; for a description see my *The Death of an Emperor* (Constable, 1989), p. 101.
17. We know this from the use of the word *chi*: the Chinese character, in its original form, showed a man turning his head away from a dish of food.
18. Stephenson, *op. cit.*, p. 223.
19. *Ibid.*, citing Ibn Tulun, *Mufakahat al-Khullan fi Hawadith al-Zaman*, Part I, p. 375.
20. Anthony Aveni, *Skywatchers of Ancient Mexico* (University of Texas Press, 1980), p. 75.

Chapter 5 The Solution from Physics

1. See for example G. J. Toomer, 'A survey of the Toledan Tables', *Osiris*, 1968, Vol. 15, pp. 1–174.
2. It would be another century before the actual diameter of the orbit, about 300 million km, became known.
3. The full title is *Astronomia nova Seu Physica Coelestis, tradita commentariis de Motibus stellae Martis* ('The New Astronomy, Based upon Causes, or Celestial Physics, Treated by Means of Commentaries on the Motions of the Star Mars'). A modern edition is *The New Astronomy*, translated by William Donahue (Cambridge University Press, 1989).
4. Robert Hooke, 'Attempt to prove the motion of the Earth', in *Lectiones Cutlerianae* (London, 1679), reprinted in R. T. Gunter, *Early Science in Oxford*, Vol. 8 (Oxford University Press, 1931). These three suppositions are as cited in Michael Hoskin (editor), *The Cambridge Illustrated History of Astronomy* (Cambridge University Press, 1997), pp. 148–9.
5. Huygens showed that where P is the inward pull on the string, r its length and v the velocity of the stone,

$$P = K_0 v^2 / r.$$

According to Kepler's third law, where T is the period of a satellite in a circular orbit, and r, the radius of the orbit,

$$T^2 = K_1 r^3,$$

with (K_0 and K_1 representing constants). Now the circumference of a circle is $2\pi r$, so that the time T taken for a complete circuit at a velocity, v, is $2\pi r/v$ which is equivalent to

$$Tv = 2\pi r,$$

so that

$$T^2v^2 = 4\pi^2r^2.$$

Substituting for T^2 from Kepler's third law,

$$K_1r^3v^2 = 4\pi^2r^2,$$

whence, dividing both sides by r^4,

$$K_1v^2/r = 4\pi^2/r^2,$$

so that Huygens' pull P ($= K_0v^2/r$), is in inverse proportion to the square of the radius, r.

6. The dealings between Hooke, Halley and Newton are recounted in Hoskin, *op. cit.*, pp. 154–7,

7. Its actual value is 6.67×10^{-11} N m^2/kg^2.

8. Cited by Hoskin, *op. cit.*, p. 158.

9. The Earth's mass is approximately 81 times the Moon's; Jupiter's mass, by comparison, is some 2,600 times that of its largest moon, Ganymede.

10. The actual values are 6378.160 km for the equatorial radius, and 6356.775 km for the polar radius.

11. In the event, navigation based on lunar tables never became a practical proposition. In part this was because the necessary instruments were difficult to use, but the main reason was the invention in 1764 by John Harrison (1693–1776) of the completely reliable H-4 marine chronometer, the usefulness of which was demonstrated on Captain James Cook's second voyage (1772–5) to the Pacific. To determine longitude with the aid of the H-4, it was necessary only to measure the altitude of stars above the horizon at a known time, the accuracy of which was guaranteed by the chronometer. This was a much simpler operation to carry out at sea, and the required astronomical tables

were also published annually in *The Abridged Nautical Almanac*. Harrison eventually received £20,000, in prizes of a quite different order to those awarded to Mayer and Euler.

Chapter 6 The Gateway to Discovery

1. Leslie V. Morrison *et al.*, 'Diameter of the Sun in AD 1715', *Nature*, 4 February 1988, Vol. 331, p. 421.
2. Leon Golub and Jay M. Pasachoff, *The Solar Corona* (Cambridge University Press, 1997), pp. 132–133.
3. J. B. Zirker in his *Total Eclipses of the Sun* (Van Nostrand Reinhold, 1984), records the range of this research, and provides much of the material for this chapter.
4. Auguste Comte, *Cours de philosophie positive* (Paris, 1835), 11, 8.
5. Michael Hoskin (editor), *The Cambridge Illustrated History of Astronomy* (Cambridge University Press, 1997), p. 195.
6. Golub and Pasachoff, *op. cit.*, p. 25.
7. The multiple is now known to be equal to 3.29×10^{15}/second.
8. The quotations are from Abraham Pais, *Niels Bohr's Times, in Physics, Philosophy and Polity* (Clarendon Press, 1991), pp. 145, 147.
9. The value of h is 6.626×10^{-34} joule.second.
10. Albert Einstein, 'Grundlage der allgemeinen Relativitätstheorie', *Annalen der Physik*, 1916, Vol. 49, pp. 769–822. The title means 'The foundations of the theory of general relativity'.
11. Bernhard Riemann, 'Über die Hypothesen, welche der Geometrie zu Grunde liegen', in *Gesammelte mathematische Werke*, 2nd edition (Teubner, 1982), pp. 272–87. The title translates as 'On the hypotheses that lie at the foundation of geometry'.
12. Quoted in Ronald Clark, *Einstein: The Life and Times* (Hodder & Stoughton, 1979), p. 203.
13. Willem de Sitter, 'On Einstein's theory of gravitation, and its astronomical consequences', *Monthly Notices of the Royal Astronomical Society*, 1916, Vol. 76, pp. 699–728.
14. Quoted in Clark, *op. cit.*, p. 226.
15. This and the previous two quotations are from Clark, *op. cit.*, p. 228.
16. Quoted in Zirker, *op. cit.*, p. 182.

17. Gerard 't Hooft, *In Search of the Ultimate Building Blocks* (Cambridge University Press, 1997), p. 117.
18. F. R. Stephenson, *Historical Eclipses and Earth's Rotation* (Cambridge University Press, 1997).
19. Quoted in W. Ley, *Kant's Cosmogony* (Greenwood, 1968), p. 173.
20. Quoted in Stephenson, *Op. cit.*, p. 7.
21. E. Liais, *Mémoires de l'Académie*, 1866, Vol. 28, pp. 1119–21. Quoted in English in Stephenson, *Op. cit.*, p. 12.
22. Stephenson, *Op. cit.*, pp. 540–48.
23. *Ibid.*, p. 517.

Chapter 7 The Problem of Time and Space

1. Quoted in Shigeru Nakayama, *A History of Japanese Astronomy* (Harvard University Press, 1969), p. 158.
2. W. M. Smart, *Textbook on Spherical Astronomy*, 6th edition revised by R. M. Green (Cambridge University Press, 1977), p. 420.
3. F. Espenak and J. Anderson, *Total Solar Eclipse of 1999 August 11*, NASA Reference Publication 1398 (NASA, March 1997), Table 3: 'Path of the umbral shadow'. This table may be accessed on the Internet at http://sunearth.gsfc.nasa.gov/eclipse/TSE1999.Tab3.html, though this address may change.
4. Because the calendar year does not keep pace with the sidereal year, the vernal equinox sometimes falls on 20 or 22 March.
5. At the autumnal equinox, on or around 21 September – when the Sun crosses the celestial equator from north to south – the Sun will again be overhead as viewed from a point on the equator at midday. It will then lie in the constellation Virgo, at a point on the celestial sphere directly opposite Υ, which will therefore be directly overhead at midnight. From any point in the northern hemisphere, millennial stargazers can locate Υ by taking the pole star, at local midnight, to establish their own meridian. Υ will then lie in the south, on the local meridian, 90° from the pole star (the right angle can be determined by using a set square as an astrolabe). The actual position of Υ may be difficult to locate in this rough-and-ready manner, but the constellation in which it is located, Pisces, should be easy to identify with the help of a star chart.

6. Harold Spencer Jones, 'The rotation of the Earth, and the secular accelerations of the Sun, Moon and planets', *Monthly Notices of the Royal Astronomical Society*, 1939, Vol. 99, pp. 541–8.

7. The use of Julian centuries may seem perverse given the adoption of the Gregorian calendar in 1582, but astronomers find the length of the Julian century, 365.25 days, easier to work with. The coefficients in the formula take into account the discrepancy between the two calendars.

8. *Transactions of the International Astronomical Union*, 1954, Vol. 8, p. 80.

9. The definition was formally adopted by the 13th General Conference on Weights and Measures, 1967.

10. Note that this would be the exact time of midnight only at one particular longitude.

11. Espenak and Anderson, *Op. cit.*, Table 2: 'Shadow contact and circumstances, total solar eclipse of 1999 August 11'. This table also contains the following definitions (note that TDT is Terrestrial Dynamical Time, and UT Universal Time): 'Ephemeris longitude is the terrestrial dynamic longitude assuming a uniformly rotating Earth. True longitude is calculated by correcting the ephemeris longitude for the non-uniform rotation of the Earth. (TL = EL − 1.002 738 × T/240, where T (in seconds) = TDT − UT.)

12. Albert Einstein, *Ideas and Opinions* (Wing Books, New York, 1954), p. 361.

13. *Ibid.*, p. 362.

14. *Ibid.*, p. 349.

15. It seems that in ancient Babylon the same word could be used to refer to both lightning and the phenomenon of totality during a total solar eclipse (F. R. Stephenson, *Historical Eclipses and Earth's Rotation* (Cambridge University Press, 1997, p. 144).

16. This system of reckoning years according to the reign of the monarch persisted into modern times, even in Britain: the practice of dating UK Acts of Parliament according to so-called regnal years ceased as recently as 1962.

17. Herbert J. Spinden, 'Diffusion of Mayan chronology', in *The Maya and Their Neighbors* (Dover Publications, 1977), p. 171.

18. A period of 52 years is equivalent to 18,980 days, and 18,980 is the lowest common multiple of 260 and 362.

19. Anthony Aveni, *Skywatchers of Ancient Mexico* (University of Texas Press, 1980), p. 182.

20. Thomas Crump, *The Anthropology of Numbers* (Cambridge University Press, 1991), p. 86.

Chapter 8 History, Sacred and Profane

1. Amos viii:9.

2. Quoted in Clarence Darrow, *Attorney for the Damned*, edited by Arthur Weinberg (Simon & Schuster, 1957), pp. 174–5.

3. Genesis 1:xiv–xix.

4. Joshua x:12–13.

5. Joel ii:30–31.

6. E. C. Krupp, 'When worlds collide: The Velikovsky catastrophe', in *In Search of Ancient Astronomies*, edited by E. C. Krupp (Penguin, 1984), pp. 220-30.

7. Quoted in Angela Partington (editor), *The Oxford Dictionary of Quotations*, 4th edition (Oxford University Press, 1992), p. 353.

8. Isaiah xlv:15.

9. Luke xxiii:44. The last five words quoted here do not appear in the corresponding accounts in Matthew and Mark.

10. J. F. A. Sawyer, 'Why is a solar eclipse mentioned in the Passion narrative (Luke XXIII.44–5)?', *Journal of Theological Studies*, 1972, Vol. 23, pp. 124–8.

11. G. R. Driver, 'Two problems in the New Testament', *Journal of Theological Studies* (New Series), 1964, Vol. 16, p. 334.

12. Daniel ii:12f.

13. Daniel ii:27–8.

14. Daniel v:25.

15. Isaiah xlvii:13.

16. H. Hunger, *Astrological Reports to the Assyrian Kings*, State Archives of Assyria, Vol. VIII (Helsinki University Press, 1992), p. 220.

17. From the *Shu Ching* ('Historical Classic'), quoted in Joseph Needham, *The Shorter Science and Civilisation in China*, Vol. 2, abridged by Colin A. Ronan (Cambridge University Press, 1981), p. 73.

18. Needham, *op. cit.*, pp. 195–6.

19. The *National Geographic Magazine* for March 1949 reproduces on p. 343 a painting from Thailand made on the occasion of the solar eclipse of 9 May 1948, showing the demon Phra Rahu taking a bite out of the Sun.

20. Quoted in Needham, *op. cit.*, p. 200.

21. *Ibid.*, p. 203.

22. *Ibid.*, p. 204.

23. Quoted in F. R. Stephenson, *Historical Eclipses and Earth's Rotation* (Cambridge University Press, 1997).

24. Quoted in *ibid.*, pp. 241–2.

25. *Ibid.*, pp. 234, 237.

26. Shigeru Nakayama, *A History of Japanese Astronomy* (Harvard University Press, 1969), p. 51.

27. Pindar, *Paean*, translated by J. Sandys (Heinemann, 1978), ix.

28. Marinus, *Life of Proclus*, Chapter 37, in *The Philosophy of Proclus*, translated by L. J. Rosan (Cosmos, New York, 1949), p. 34.

29. Livy, *The Founding of the City*, translated by E. T. Sage (Heinemann, 1936), XXXVIII 36, 4.

30. The passage quoted here, and those not otherwise attributed in the following paragraphs, are from Stephenson, *op. cit.*, Chapter 11 'Eclipse records from medieval Europe'.

31. E. Walter Maunder (editor), *The Total Solar Eclipse 1900* (British Astronomical Association, 1901), p. 214.

32. *The Eclipse Chasers* was transmitted in three parts, on 31 March, 9 April and 16 April 1996. I am most grateful to Phil Whitaker for lending me his video recording of these programmes (which were plainly useful to him in writing his novel *Eclipse of the Sun*).

33. This eclipse is analysed in detail in Stephenson, *op. cit.*, p. 348f.

34. Nakayama, *op. cit.*, p. 51.

35. Quoted in Martin Palmer, *Tu'ung Shu: The Ancient Chinese Almanac* (Rider, London, 1986), p. 23.

36. F. W. Hodge (editor), *Handbook of American Indians North of Mexico* (Government Printing Office, Washington, 1910), pp. 731–2.

Chapter 9 Anthropologists and Travellers

1. Dennis Breedlove and Robert Laughlin, *The Flowering of Man: A Tzotzil Botany of Zinacantan*, Smithsonian Contributions to Anthropology No. 35, 2 vols (Smithsonian Institution, 1993).
2. The first three volumes are listed in the Bibliography.
3. Claude Lévi-Strauss, *Introduction to a Science of Mythology*, Vol. 1 *From Honey to Ashes* (Harper & Row, 1973), p. 270.
4. Ruth Finnegan, 'Oral literature', in *Encyclopedia of Social and Cultural Anthropology*, edited by Alan Barnard and Jonathan Spencer (Routledge, 1996), p. 405.
5. Claude Lévi-Strauss, *Introduction to a Science of Mythology*, Vol. 2 *The Origin of Table Manners* (Harper & Row, 1973), p. 181.
6. Claude Lévi-Strauss, *Introduction to a Science of Mythology*, Vol. 3 *The Raw and the Cooked* (Harper & Row, 1973), p. 287.
7. Lévi-Strauss, *From Honey to Ashes*, p. 442.
8. Lévi-Strauss, *The Origin of Table Manners*, p. 42.
9. *Ibid.*, p. 220.
10. Lévi-Strauss, *The Raw and the Cooked*, p. 288.
11. Gary Gossen, *Chamulas in the World of the Sun: Time and Space in a Maya Oral Tradition* (Harvard University Press, 1974).
12. Cornelius Osgood, *Ingalik Social Culture*, Yale University Publications in Anthropology Vol. 53 (Yale University Press, 1958), pp. 65–6.
13. Calvin Martin, *Keepers of the Game: Indian-Animal Relationships and the Fur Trade* (University of California Press, Berkeley, 1987), p. 39.
14. Quoted in J. C. Beaglehole, *The Life of Captain James Cook* (Stanford University Press, 1974), p. 87. The text fails to make clear that the eclipse was only partial in England.
15. E. Walter Maunder, *The Indian Eclipse 1898* (British Astronomical Association, 1899), p. 6.
16. *Ibid.*, p. 57.
17. Rider Haggard, *King Solomon's Mines* (Oxford University Press, 1989).
18. *Ibid.*, Introduction by Denis Butts, p. vii.
19. This and the previous quotation are from Haggard, *Op. cit.*, p. 174.

20. Mark Twain, *A Connecticut Yankee in King Arthur's Court*, edited by B. L. Stein (University of California Press, Berkeley, 1979), p. 86.
21. Quoted in *ibid.*, Introduction by H. N. Smith, p. 25.
22. Hergé, *The Sun Temple* (Methuen, 1949).
23. Phil Whitaker, *Eclipse of the Sun* (Orion, 1997), p. 231.
24. Edward Said, *Orientalism* (Penguin, 1995), p. 3 [1st edition Routledge & Kegan Paul, 1978].
25. *Ibid.*, p. 7.
26. Rudyard Kipling, *Kim* (Penguin, 1987), Introduction by Edward Said, p. 23.
27. Pauline Melville, *The Ventriloquist's Tale* (Bloomsbury, 1997).
28. Lévi Strauss, *The Raw and the Cooked*, p. 296. (Melville, who gives no reference for her quotation, has shortened the original.)
29. J. Bernlef, *Eclips* (Querido, 1993) [English translation published as *Eclipse* (Faber, 1996)].
30. Christopher Hampton, *Total Eclipse* (Faber, 1997).
31. Ian Cole, *The Eclipse of Council Housing* (Routledge, 1993).
32. Lee Smith, *Me and My Baby View the Eclipse* (Random House, 1991).
33. Tony Walter, *Eclipse of Eternity* (Routledge, 1996).
34. Bryan Turner, quoted in *ibid.*, p. vi.
35. *Ibid.*, p. 5.
36. *Ibid.*, p. 192.
37. *Ibid.*, p. 195.
38. Sheridan Williams, *UK Solar Eclipses from the Year 1* (Clock Tower Press, Leighton Buzzard, 1996), A2–A3.
39. William Shakespeare, *King Lear*, Act 1, Scene 2.
40. John Milton, *Paradise Lose*, Book I, lines 594–9.

Bibliography

Airy, G. B., 'On the results of recent calculations on the eclipse of Thales and the eclipses connected with it', in *Royal Institution Library of Science*, Vol. 1, Astronomy, (Royal Institution, 1853).

Aveni, Anthony, *Skywatchers of Ancient Mexico* (University of Texas Press, 1980).

Beaglehole, J. C., *The Life of Captain James Cook* (Stanford University Press, 1974).

Bell, Steve, *The RGO Guide to the 1999 Total Eclipse of the Sun* (Cambridge, HM Nautical Almanac Office, 1997).

Bernlef, J., *Eclips* (Querido, 1993) [English translation published as *Eclipse* (Faber, 1996)].

Breedlove, Dennis and Laughlin, Robert, *The Flowering of Man: A Tzotzil Botany of Zinacantan*, Smithsonian Contributions to Anthropology No. 35, 2 vols (Smithsonian Institution, 1993).

Brewer, Bryan, *Eclipse* (Earth View, Seattle, 1991).

Clark, Ronald W., *Einstein: The Life and Times* (Hodder & Stoughton, 1979).

Cole, Ian, *The Eclipse of Council Housing* (Routledge, 1993).

Comte, Auguste, *Cours de philosophie positive* (Paris, 1835).

Crump, Thomas, *The Death of an Emperor* (Constable, 1989).

Crump, Thomas, *The Anthropology of Numbers* (Cambridge University Press, 1991).

243

Darrow, Clarence, *Attorney for the Damned*, edited by Arthur Weinberg (Simon & Schuster, 1957).

de Sitter, W., 'On Einstein's theory of gravitation, and its astronomical consequences', *Monthly Notices of the Royal Astronomical Society*, 1916, Vol. 76, pp. 699–728.

Driver, G. R., 'Two problems in the New Testament', *Journal of Theological Studies* (New Series), 1964, Vol. 16, pp. 333–7.

Einstein, A., 'Grundlage der allgemeinen Relativitätstheorie', *Annalen der Physik*, 1916, Vol. 49, pp. 769–822.

Einstein, Albert, *Ideas and Opinions* (Wing Books, New York, 1954).

Espenak, F. and Anderson, J., *Total Solar Eclipse of 1999 August 11*, NASA Reference Publication 1398 (NASA, March 1997).

Finnegan, Ruth, 'Oral literature', in *Encyclopedia of Social and Cultural Anthropology*, edited by Alan Barnard and Jonathan Spencer (Routledge, 1996).

Fotheringham, J. K., 'A solution of ancient eclipses of the Sun', *Monthly Notices of the Royal Astronomical Society*, 1920, Vol. 81, pp. 104–26.

de Francis, John, *Visible Speech: The Oneness of Writing Systems* (University of Hawaii Press, 1989).

Golub, Leon and Pasachoff, Jay M., *The Solar Corona* (Cambridge University Press, 1997).

Gossen, Gary, *Chamulas in the World of the Sun: Time and Space in a Maya Oral Tradition* (Harvard University Press, 1974).

Gribbin, John, *Companion to the Cosmos* (Phoenix, 1997).

Haggard, Rider, *King Solomon's Mines* (Oxford University Press, 1989) [1st edition 1885].

Hampton, Christopher, *Total Eclipse* (Faber, 1997).

Hergé, *The Sun Temple* (Methuen, 1949).

Hodge, F. W. (editor), *Handbook of American Indians North of Mexico* (Government Printing Office, Washington, 1910).

't Hooft, Gerard, *In Search of the Ultimate Building Blocks* (Cambridge University Press, 1997).

Hooke, Robert, 'Attempt to prove the motion of the Earth', in *Lectiones Cutlerianae* (London, 1679), reprinted in R. T. Gunter, *Early Science in Oxford*, Vol. 8 (Oxford University Press, 1931).

Hoskin, Michael (editor), *The Cambridge Illustrated History of Astronomy* (Cambridge University Press, 1997).

Hoyle, Fred, *From Stonehenge to Modern Astronomy* (Cambridge University Press, 1971).

Hunger, H., *Astrological Reports to the Assyrian Kings*, State Archives of Assyria, Vol. VIII (Helsinki University Press, 1992).

Jones, H. Spencer, 'The rotation of the earth, and the secular accelerations of the sun, moon and planets', *Monthly Notices of the Royal Astronomical Society*, 1939, Vol. 99, pp. 541–8.

Kepler, Johannes, *The New Astronomy*, translated by William Donahue (Cambridge University Press, 1989).

Kipling, Rudyard, *Kim* (Penguin, 1987) [1st edition 1901].

Kirk, G. S., Raven, J. E. and Schofield, M., *The Presocratic Philosophers*, 2nd edition (Cambridge University Press, 1983).

Krupp, E. C., 'When worlds collide: The Velikovsky catastrophe', in *In Search of Ancient Astronomies*, edited by E. C. Krupp (Penguin, 1984), pp. 220–30.

Lévi-Strauss, Claude, *Introduction to a Science of Mythology* (Harper & Row); Vol. 1 *From Honey to Ashes* (1973), Vol. 2 *The Raw and the Cooked* (1975), Vol. 3 *The Origin of Table Manners* (1979).

Ley, W., *Kant's Cosmogony* (Greenwood, 1968).

Lieberman, Philip, *Uniquely Human* (Harvard University Press, 1991).

Livy, *The Founding of the City*, translated by E. T. Sage (Heinemann, 1936).

Malville, J. M., Wendorf, F., Mazar, A. A. and Schild, R., 'Megaliths and Neolithic astronomy in southern Egypt', *Nature*, 2 April 1998, Vol. 392, pp. 488–91.

Marinus, *Life of Proclus*, Chapter 37, in *The Philosophy of Proclus*, translated by L. J. Rosan (Cosmos, New York, 1949), p. 34.

Marshack, Alexander, 'Lunar notations on Upper Paleolithic remains', *Science*, 1964, Vol. 146, pp. 743–5.

Martin, Calvin, *Keepers of the Game: Indian-Animal Relationships and the Fur Trade* (University of California Press, Berkeley, 1978).

Maunder, E. Walter, *The Indian Eclipse 1898* (British Astronomical Association, 1899).

Maunder, E. Walter (editor), *The Total Solar Eclipse 1900* (British Astronomical Association, 1901).

Melville, Pauline, *The Ventriloquist's Tale* (Bloomsbury, 1997).

Morrison, Leslie V., Stephenson, F. Richard and Parkinson, John, 'Diameter of the Sun in AD 1715', *Nature*, 4 February 1988, Vol. 331, p. 421.

Nakayama, Shigeru, *A History of Japanese Astronomy* (Harvard University Press, 1969).

Needham, Joseph, *The Shorter Science and Civilisation in China*, Vol. 2, abridged by Colin A. Ronan (Cambridge University Press, 1981).

Newton, Isaac, *Philosophiae naturalis principia mathematica*, translated by Andrew Motte (1729) and edited by Florian Cajori (University of California Press, 1924) [1st edition 1687].

Neugebauer, Otto, *History of Ancient Mathematical Astronomy* (Springer, 1975).

North, John, *Stonehenge: Neolithic Man and the Cosmos* (Harper-Collins, 1996).

Oppolzer, Theodor von, *Canon of Eclipses* (Dover Publications, 1962) [1st edition published as *Kanon der Finsternissen* (Kaiserliche Akademie der Wissenschaft, 1887)].

Osgood, Cornelius, *Ingalik Social Culture*, Yale University Publications in Anthropology Vol. 53 (Yale University Press, 1958).

Pais, Abraham, *Niels Bohr's Times, in Physics, Philosophy and Polity* (Clarendon Press, 1991).

Palmer, Martin, *Tu'ung Shu: The Ancient Chinese Almanac* (Rider, London, 1986).

Partington, Angela (editor), *The Oxford Dictionary of Quotations*, 4th edition (Oxford University Press, 1992).

Pindar, *Paean*, translated by J. Sandys (Heinemann, 1978).

Pliny, *Naturalis historia*, translated by H. Rackham (Heinemann, 1938).

Plutarch, *Moralia*, Vol. XII, pp. 117–19, translated by H. Cherniss and W. C. Helmbold (Heinemann, 1957).

Ptolemy, *The Almagest*, translated by G. J. Toomer (Duckworth, 1984).

Riemann, G. F. B., 'Über die Hypothesen, welche der Geometrie zu Grunde liegen', in *Gesammelte mathematische Werke*, 2nd edition (Teubner, 1892), pp. 272–87.

Said, Edward, *Orientalism* (Penguin, 1995) [1st edition Routledge & Kegan Paul, 1978].

Sawyer, J. F. A., 'Why is a solar eclipse mentioned in the Passion narrative (Luke XXIII:44–5)?', *Journal of Theological Studies*, 1972, Vol. 23, pp. 124–8.

Schmandt-Besserat, Denise, The earliest precursor of writing, *Scientific American*, June 1979, pp. 38–47.

Smart, W. M., *Textbook on Spherical Astronomy*, 6th edition revised by R. M. Green (Cambridge University Press, 1977).

Smith, Lee, *Me and My Baby View the Eclipse* (Random House, 1991).

Spinden, Herbert J., 'Diffusion of Mayan chronology', in *The Maya and Their Neighbors* (Dover Publications, 1977), pp. 162–78.

Stephenson, F. R., *Historical Eclipses and Earth's Rotation* (Cambridge University Press, 1997).

Toomer, G. J., 'A survey of the Toledan Tables', *Osiris*, 1968, Vol. 15, pp. 1–174.

Twain, Mark, *A Connecticut Yankee in King Arthur's Court*, edited by B. L. Stein (University of California Press, Berkeley, 1979) [1st edition 1889].

Velikovsky, Immanuel, *Worlds in Collision* (Gollancz, 1950).

Walter, Tony, *Eclipse of Eternity* (Routledge, 1996).

Whitaker, Phil, *Eclipse of the Sun* (Orion, 1997).

Williams, Sheridan, *UK Solar Eclipses from the Year 1* (Clock Tower Press, Leighton Buzzard, 1996).

Zirker, J. B., *Total Eclipses of the Sun* (Van Nostrand Reinhold, 1984).

Index